Math Skills for Science

HOLT, RINEHART AND WINSTON
A Harcourt Education Company
Orlando • Austin • New York • San Diego • Toronto • London

To the Teacher

Math and science are often overlapping disciplines. The scientist and the science student must be able to process information logically and use known formulas and statistical procedures effectively. This booklet serves to build and reinforce the basic math skills necessary for the completion of a middle-school science course. In addition, this booklet is designed to boost student confidence in using mathematical tools to solve problems in the science classroom and beyond. By completing worksheets from this booklet, students will also gain a better understanding of the ways math skills can be applied to real-world situations. With this understanding, students should find more value, and more success, in honing their science skills.

This workbook consists of the following components:

- **Math Skills Worksheets**
  Each Math Skills worksheet gives a brief introduction to a relevant math skill, a step-by-step explanation of the math process, one or more example problems, and a variety of practice problems. The first worksheet within each Math Skill heading contains the most basic information about that math skill, with subsequent worksheets building on the topic. Although the Math Skills worksheets remain relevant to the science curriculum by using scientific language and scenarios, the emphasis of the Math Skills worksheets is on the math skill being discussed and is not intended to support any one scientific topic or skill.

- **Math in Science Worksheets**
  The Math in Science worksheets are designed to give your students practice using math in real-life scientific situations. Each Math in Science worksheet focuses on a single scientific skill or scenario and challenges the student to use science skills and math skills together to solve problems. These worksheets are subdivided into the following categories: Integrated Science, Life Science, Earth Science, and Physical Science.

- **Student Self-Assessments**
  The Student Self-Assessment on page vi of this booklet gives each student the opportunity to assess his or her own math skills. This self-assessment gives you and the student some insight into areas that are most in need of improvement. The Student Self-Assessment Revisited on page 86 can be used later to determine how much progress has been made.

- **Answer Key**
  For your convenience, an Answer Key is provided in the back of this booklet. The key includes reduced versions of all applicable worksheets, with answers included on each page.

Credits: See page 87.

Printed in the United States of America

ISBN 0-03-035198-7 1 2 3 4 5 6 085 04 03

CONTENTS

To the Teacher ii

Student Self-Assessment vi

MATH SKILLS

Addition and Subtraction

1. Addition Review 1
2. Subtraction Review 2

Multiplication

3. Multiplying Whole Numbers 3
4. A Shortcut for Multiplying Large Numbers 4

Division

5. Dividing Whole Numbers with Long Division 5
6. Checking Division with Multiplication 6

Averages

7. What Is an Average? 7
8. Average, Mode, and Median 9

Positive and Negative Numbers

9. Comparing Integers on a Number Line 11
10. Arithmetic with Positive and Negative Numbers 12

Fractions

11. What Is a Fraction? 15
12. Reducing Fractions to Lowest Terms 16
13. Improper Fractions and Mixed Numbers 17
14. Adding and Subtracting Fractions 18
15. Multiplying and Dividing Fractions 20

Ratios and Proportions

16. What Is a Ratio? 21
17. Using Proportions and Cross-Multiplication 22

Decimals

18. Decimals and Fractions 24
19. Arithmetic with Decimals 25

Percentages

20. Parts of 100: Calculating Percentages 28
21. Percentages, Fractions, and Decimals 29
22. Working with Percentages and Proportions 31

Powers of 10

23. Counting the Zeros 32
24. Creating Exponents 33

Scientific Notation
25. What Is Scientific Notation? 34
26. Multiplying and Dividing in Scientific Notation 35
SI Measurement and Conversion
27. What Is SI? 37
28. A Formula for SI Catch-up 39
Geometry
29. Finding Perimeter and Area 41
30. Finding Volume 43
The Unit Factor and Dimensional Analysis
31. The Unit Factor and Dimensional Analysis 44
Math in Science: Integrated Science
32. Density 47
(Physical Science and Earth Science)
33. The Pressure Is On! 48
(Earth Science and Physical Science)
34. Sound Reasoning 50
(Life Science and Physical Science)
35. Using Temperature Scales 51
(Earth Science and Physical Science)
36. Radioactive Decay and the Half-life 52
(Earth Science and Physical Science)
37. Rain-Forest Math 54
(Earth Science and Life Science)
Math in Science: Life Science
38. Knowing Nutrition 55
39. Random Samples: Estimating Population 58
40. Punnett Square Popcorn 60
41. Scale of Organisms 62
Math in Science: Earth Science
42. Sedimentation in the Grand Canyon 63
43. Earthquake Power! 65
44. Distances in Space 67
45. Geologic Time Scale 68
46. Mapping and Surveying 71

CONTENTS, CONTINUED

MATH IN SCIENCE: PHYSICAL SCIENCE

47. Average Speed in a Pinewood Derby 73
48. Newton: Force and Motion 74
49. Momentum 77
50. Balancing Chemical Equations 78
51. Work and Power 79
52. A Bicycle Trip 81
53. Mechanical Advantage 83
54. Color at Light Speed 84

Student Self-Assessment Revisited 86

ANSWER KEY 87

Name ______________________________ Date ____________ Class ____________

Student Self-Assessment

Before doing any of the worksheets in this booklet, rate your math skills.

Math skill	Good	OK	Needs improvement	Don't know
Addition				
Subtraction				
Multiplication				
Division				
Averages				
Positive and negative numbers				
Fractions				
Ratios				
Proportions				
Decimals				
Percentages				
Powers of 10				
Scientific notation				
SI measurement and conversion				
Dimensional analysis				
Geometry				

Can you think of a time when you have used math to solve a problem in your science class? Describe it below.

____

____

Name ______________________ Date ____________ Class ____________

WORKSHEET

1 **MATH SKILLS**

Addition Review

Addition is used to find the total of two or more quantities. The answer to an addition problem is known as the *sum.*

PROCEDURE: To find the sum of a set of numbers, align the numbers vertically so that the ones digits are in the same column. Add each column, working from right to left.

SAMPLE PROBLEM: Find the sum of 317, 435, and 92.

Step 1: Add the ones. Don't forget to carry your numbers.	**Step 2:** Add the tens.	**Step 3:** Add the hundreds.
1 317 435 + 92 4	1 1 317 435 + 92 44	1 317 435 + 92 844

The sum is **844.**

Add It Up!

1. Find the sums of the following problems:

a. 348 + 21 = ______

b. 98,125 + 233 = ______

c. 593 + 386 = ______

d. 36,186 + 27,309 = ______

2. Your doctor advises you to take 60 mg of vitamin C, 20 mg of niacin, and 15 mg of zinc every day. How many milligrams of nutrients will you take?

____

3. A chemistry experiment calls for 356 mL of water, 197 mL of saline solution, and 55 mL of vinegar. How much liquid is needed in all?

____

4. Between 1980 and 1992, the population of San Bernardino County, CA, increased by 639,327 people. If the population in 1980 was 895,016, what was the population in 1992?

____

5. Halley's comet returns to our solar system every 76 years. Its last visit was in 1986. What year will it appear again?

____

Name ______________________________ Date ______________ Class ______________

WORKSHEET

2 **MATH SKILLS**

Subtraction Review

Subtraction is used to take one number from another number. The answer to a subtraction problem is known as the *difference*. The difference is how much larger or smaller one number is than the other.

PROCEDURE: To find the difference between two numbers, first align the numbers vertically so that the ones digits are in the same column, with the larger number above the smaller number. Subtract, working from right to left, one column at a time. Remember to borrow when necessary.

SAMPLE PROBLEM: Find the difference between 622 and 348.

Step 1: Subtract the ones, borrowing when necessary.

$$\begin{array}{r} 62^{1}\mathbf{2} \\ -\ 34^{5}\mathbf{8} \\ \hline \mathbf{4} \end{array}$$

Step 2: Subtract the tens, borrowing when necessary.

$$\begin{array}{r} 6^{1}\mathbf{2}^{1}2 \\ -\ \not{3}^{4}\mathbf{4}^{5}8 \\ \hline \mathbf{7}\ 4 \end{array}$$

Step 3: Subtract the hundreds.

$$\begin{array}{r} \mathbf{6}^{1}2^{1}2 \\ -\ \not{\mathbf{3}}^{4}4^{5}8 \\ \hline \mathbf{2}\ 7\ 4 \end{array}$$

The difference of the numbers is **274.**

Take It Away!

1. Find the difference in the following problems:

a. $\begin{array}{r} 88 \\ -\ 36 \\ \hline \end{array}$ ________

b. $\begin{array}{r} 1695 \\ -\ 352 \\ \hline \end{array}$ ________

c. $\begin{array}{r} 47{,}220 \\ -\ 36{,}195 \\ \hline \end{array}$ ________

d. $\begin{array}{r} 6048 \\ -\ 3724 \\ \hline \end{array}$ ________

2. 571 − 338 = ____________________

3. 8317 − 211 = ____________________

4. Mars has a diameter of 6790 km. The diameter of Jupiter is 142,984 km. How much larger is the diameter of Jupiter than the diameter of Mars?

____

5. A horse is born with a mass of 36 kg. It is expected to have a mass of 495 kg when fully grown. How much mass will it gain?

____

6. Traveling with the wind, a plane reaches a speed of 212 m/s. On the return trip, the same plane flies into the wind and achieves a speed of only 179 m/s. How much faster does the plane fly with the wind?

____

Name ______________________ Date __________ Class __________

WORKSHEET

3 MATH SKILLS

Multiplying Whole Numbers

Suppose every student in your class planted 5 seeds in your school's garden. How many seeds were planted? You could repeatedly add 5 seeds plus 5 seeds until every student's seeds had been added, but this would be pretty time consuming. **Multiplication**, which simplifies addition, is the process of calculating the total of a number that is added together a specific number of times. For example, 3×4 means adding 3 together 4 times, or $3 + 3 + 3 + 3 = 12$. So $3 \times 4 = 12$. The answer to a multiplication problem is called the *product*.

PROCEDURE: To find the product of two whole numbers, align your numbers so that the ones digits are in the same column. Multiply each digit of the top number by the ones digit in the bottom number, carrying when necessary. Then multiply each digit in the top number by the tens in the bottom number, regrouping when necessary. Finally, add the partial products to find the final product.

SAMPLE PROBLEM: Find the product of 34 and 16.

Step 1: Align the numbers vertically. Multiply each digit in the top number by the ones digit in the bottom number. Carry when necessary.

$$\begin{array}{r} {}^{2}\mathbf{34} \\ \times\ \mathbf{16} \\ \hline \mathbf{204} \end{array}$$

Step 2: Multiply each digit in the top number by the tens in the bottom number. Imagine adding a zero in the ones column as a place holder.

$$\begin{array}{r} \mathbf{34} \\ \times\ \mathbf{16} \\ \hline 204 \\ \mathbf{34}0 \end{array}$$

Step 3: Add the partial products.

$$\begin{array}{r} 34 \\ \times\ 16 \\ \hline \mathbf{204} \\ +\ \mathbf{34}0 \\ \hline \mathbf{544} \end{array}$$

The product is **544**.

Practice Your Skills!

1. Multiply. Don't forget to show all your work.

a. $\begin{array}{r} 12 \\ \times\ 24 \\ \hline \end{array}$ **b.** $\begin{array}{r} 245 \\ \times\ 36 \\ \hline \end{array}$ **c.** $\begin{array}{r} 46 \\ \times\ 87 \\ \hline \end{array}$ **d.** $\begin{array}{r} 2751 \\ \times\ 11 \\ \hline \end{array}$

2. A farm produces 864 bushels of corn per square kilometer. The farmer plants 127 km^2 of corn. How many bushels of corn will the farm produce?

____

3. A bee travels 147 m one way from its hive to the garden. If the bee makes 93 round trips between the hive and the garden, how far will it have traveled? Be careful!

____

____

MATH SKILLS

Name ______________________ Date ____________ Class ____________

WORKSHEET

4 **MATH SKILLS**

A Shortcut for Multiplying Large Numbers

Imagine that you are a doctor doing research on white blood cells. You know that there are approximately 80,000 white blood cells in 1 mL of blood. You have a sample of 50 mL of blood. How many white blood cells are in the sample? You could multiply to find the answer, of course, but it's a large number and you need an answer quickly. How can you make this easier? Read on to learn an easy way to find the product of large numbers.

PROCEDURE: To find the product of large numbers, remove the zeros at the end of one or both numbers. Next, multiply the non-zero numbers. Finally, at the end of the product, replace the same number of zeros that you removed from your multipliers.

SAMPLE PROBLEM: Multiply 80,000 by 50.

Step 1: Remove the zeros from the end of your numbers, and multiply the non-zero numbers.

80,000 → 8~~0,000~~ → 8

× 5

50 → 5~~0~~ → 40

Step 2: At the end of your product, replace the total number of zeros you removed from the multipliers. Because you removed a total of five zeros from your multipliers, place five zeros after your product.

80,000 × 50 = 4,0**00,000**

It's Your Turn!

Using the method above, find the products of the following problems, and write the corresponding letter from the correct answer on the line.

1. 300 × 90,000	____________	**A.** 31,720,000
2. 45 × 8500	____________	**B.** 3,524,000
3. 4400 × 7500	____________	**C.** 27,000,000
4. 52,000 × 610	____________	**D.** 33,000,000
5. 88,100 × 40	____________	**E.** 382,500

Challenge Yourself!

A super-fast chess computer can perform 200,000,000 calculations per second. How many calculations can it perform in the 3 minutes it is allowed for each move?

____

____

Name ______________________ Date ____________ Class ____________

WORKSHEET

5 **MATH SKILLS**

Dividing Whole Numbers with Long Division

Long division, which is used to divide numbers of more than one digit, is really just a series of simple division, multiplication, and subtraction problems. The number that you divide is called the *dividend.* The number you divide the dividend by is the *divisor.* The answer to a division problem is called a *quotient.*

SAMPLE PROBLEM: Divide 564 by 12, or $12\overline{)564}$.

Step 1: Because you cannot divide 12 into 5, you must start by dividing 12 into 56. To do this, ask yourself, "What number multiplied by 12 comes closest to 56 without going over?" 4 × 12 = 48, so place a 4 in the quotient.

$$\begin{array}{r} 4 \\ 12\overline{)564} \end{array}$$

Step 2: Multiply the 4 by the divisor and place the product under the 56. Then subtract that product from 56.

$$\begin{array}{r} 4 \\ 12\overline{)564} \\ \underline{-48} \\ 8 \end{array}$$

Step 3: Bring the next digit down from the dividend (4), and divide this new number (84) by the divisor, as you did in Step 1. Because 12 divides into 84 seven times, write 7 in the quotient.

$$\begin{array}{r} 47 \\ 12\overline{)564} \\ \underline{-48\downarrow} \\ 84 \\ \underline{-84} \\ 0 \end{array}$$

The quotient is **47.**

Divide It Up!

1. Fill in the blanks in the following long-division problems:

a.

$$\begin{array}{r} \square 1 \\ 13\overline{)663} \\ \underline{\square 5} \\ \square 3 \\ \underline{1\square} \\ \square \end{array}$$

b.

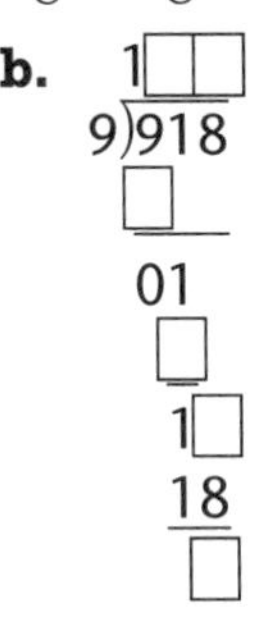

c.

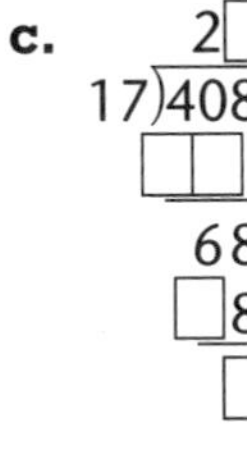

2. Complete the following long-division problems on a separate sheet of paper:

a. 3575 ÷ 11 = ______________ **b.** $52\overline{)1664}$ = ______________

c. $3\overline{)2940}$ = ______________ **d.** 4630 ÷ 5 = ______________

Name ______________________ Date ____________ Class ____________

WORKSHEET

6 MATH SKILLS

Checking Division with Multiplication

Multiplication and division "undo" one another. This means that when you ask yourself, "What is 12 divided by 3?" it is the same as asking, "What number *multiplied* by 3 gives 12?" You can use this method to catch mistakes in your division.

PROCEDURE: To check your division with multiplication, multiply the quotient of your division problem by the divisor and compare the result with the dividend. If they are equal, your division was correct.

SAMPLE PROBLEM 1: Divide 564 by 47, and check your result with multiplication.

Step 1: Divide to find your quotient.	**Step 2:** Multiply the quotient by the divisor.	**Step 3:** Compare the product with your dividend.
$\begin{array}{r} 12 \\ 47\overline{)564} \\ -47 \\ \hline 94 \\ -94 \\ \hline 0 \end{array}$	$\begin{array}{r} {}^{1} \\ 12 \\ \times\ 47 \\ \hline {}_{1}84 \\ 48 \\ \hline 564 \end{array}$	**564** = **564** Correct!

Check It Out!

Complete the following divisions, and check your math by multiplying the quotient by your divisor. Are the product and the dividend equal?

1. $15\overline{)405}$

quotient
× *divisor*

quotient = ________ product = ____________

2. $14\overline{)1694}$

quotient
× *divisor*

quotient = ________ product = ____________

3. $12\overline{)252}$

quotient
× *divisor*

quotient = ________ product = ____________

Name ______________________ Date ____________ Class ____________

WORKSHEET

7 MATH SKILLS

What Is an Average?

Suppose that your class is doing an experiment to determine the boiling point of a particular liquid. Working in groups, your classmates come up with several answers that are all slightly different. Your teacher asks you to determine which temperature best represents all of the varying results from the class. A mathematical tool called an **average**, or *mean,* will help you solve the problem. An average allows you to simplify a list of numbers into a single number that *approximates* the value of all of them. Check it out!

PROCEDURE: To calculate the average of any set of numbers, first add all of the numbers to find the sum. Then divide the sum by the amount of numbers in your set. The result is the average of your numbers.

SAMPLE PROBLEM: Find the average of the following set of numbers:

5, 4, 7, 8

Step 1: Find the sum.

$$5 + 4 + 7 + 8 = \mathbf{24}$$

Step 2: Divide the sum by the amount of numbers in your set. Because there are four numbers in your set, divide the sum by 4.

$$24 \div 4 = 6 \text{ or } \frac{24}{4} = \mathbf{6}$$

The average of the numbers is **6.**

Practice Your Skills!

Be sure to show your work for the following problems:

1. Find the average of each of the following sets of numbers.

a. 19 m, 11 m, 29 m, 62 m, 14 m

____

____

b. 12 cm, 16 cm, 25 cm, 15 cm

____

____

c. 31°C, 42°C, 35°C, 38°C, 59°C

____

____

MATH SKILLS

Use the data in the tables to complete the following problems. Be sure to show your work.

Height of Students (cm)

Students	Grade 6	Grade 7	Grade 8	Grade 9
Gretchen	152	156	159	163
Dylan	151	152	157	162
Sergio	144	147	150	152

2. Calculate the average of Gretchen's and Dylan's heights in the 8th grade.

____

____

3. What is the average height of all three students in Grade 6?

____

____

Number of Wildfires in 1993–1996

Year	Arizona	New Mexico	Oklahoma	Texas
1993	10	7	17	85
1994	16	11	24	84
1995	12	5	7	72
1996	13	5	37	91

4. What was the average number of wildfires to occur annually in New Mexico for the years 1993–1996?

____

____

5. What was the average number of wildfires for all four states in 1995?

____

____

6. What was the average number of wildfires to occur annually in Texas for the years 1993–1996?

____

____

Name ______________________ Date ____________ Class ____________

WORKSHEET

8 MATH SKILLS

Average, Mode, and Median

Although an average, or mean, is the most common way to simplify a list of numbers, there are other mathematical tools that can help you work with lists of numbers. **Mode** is the number or value that appears most often in a particular set of numbers. **Median** is the number that falls in the *numerical center* of a list of numbers. Read on to find out how to find mode and median.

PROCEDURE: *To find the mode,* list your numbers in numerical order. Then determine which number appears most often in the set. That number is the mode. **Note:** A list of numbers may have more than one mode. If no number appears more often than the others, that series of numbers does not have a mode.

SAMPLE PROBLEM: Find the mode of 4, 3, 6, 10, and 3.

Step 1: List the numbers in numerical order.

3, 3, 4, 6, 10

Step 2: Determine the number that appears most often in the set.

3, 3, 4, 6, 10

The mode of 4, 3, 6, 10, and 3 is **3.**

PROCEDURE: *To find the median,* list the numbers in numerical order. Next determine the number that appears in the middle of the set. **Note:** If more than one number falls in the middle, the median is the average of those numbers.

SAMPLE PROBLEM: Find the median of 25, 22, 24, 19, 25, 14, 26, and 15.

Step 1: List the numbers in numerical order.

14, 15, 19, 22, 24, 25, 25, 26

Step 2: Determine which number falls in the middle of the set.

14, 15, 19, 22, 24, 25, 25, 26

Because two numbers fall in the middle (22 and 24), the median is their average.

Median = (22 + 24) ÷ 2 = **23**

Get in the Mode!

1. Find the mode and median for the following sets of numbers:

a. 37, 30, 35, 37, 32, 40, 34

Mode ________ Median ________

b. 19, 29, 9, 12, 10

Mode ________ Median ________

c. 109, 84, 88, 107, 84, 94

Mode ________ Median ________

d. 26, 53, 39, 53, 49, 56, 35, 26

Mode ________ Median ________

e. 25 m, 24 m, 27 m, 27 m, 49 m, 47 m, 45 m

Mode ________ Median ________

f. 98 L, 99 L, 101 L, 111 L, 132 L, 103 L

Mode ________ Median ________

MATH SKILLS

Peregrine Falcons—How Fast Can They Fly?

The peregrine falcon is the fastest bird in the world. It can reach speeds of almost 300 km/h when hunting. An ornithologist, a scientist who studies birds, has gathered the data in the chart below to try to learn exactly how fast the falcons can fly. Use what you have learned about averages, modes, and medians to analyze some of the birds' top speeds.

Falcon Flight Speeds*

Day	Falcon A	Falcon B	Falcon C	Falcon D	Falcon E
1	189	199	211	253	199
2	275	261	241	235	279
3	262	225	271	190	271
4	203	199	223	185	265
5	241	227	209	199	253
6	222	240	265	253	232
7	203	203	240	260	279

*All flight speeds are in km/h.

2. What was the average top speed of Falcon B for the entire week?

____

____

3. What were the modes for Falcon D and Falcon E for the entire week?

____

____

4. Which had a faster median speed for the week, Falcon A or Falcon B?

____

____

____

5. What were the median speeds for Falcon B and Falcon D for days 1–6?

____

____

____

Name ______________________ Date __________ Class __________

WORKSHEET

9 MATH SKILLS

Comparing Integers on a Number Line

An **integer** is any whole number (0, 1, 2, 3, . . .) or its opposite. A good way to compare integers is with a *number line,* which is used to represent positive and negative numbers in order. A number line looks like this:

The farther a number is to the right on a number line, the greater the number. The farther a number is to the left on a number line, the smaller the number.

PROCEDURE: To compare integers on a number line, simply place your values on the line, with positive numbers to the right of zero and negative numbers to the left of zero. The number that is the farthest to the right is the greatest number. The number that is the farthest to the left is the smallest number.

SAMPLE PROBLEM: Which is greater, −8 or −3?

Step 1: Draw your number line and select a point for 0. Then fill in the integer values on the line.

Step 2: Place the integers you are comparing on the number line. Because both numbers are negative, they will both be to the left of zero.

Because −3 is farther to the right than −8, **−3** is greater than −8.

Practice Your Skills!

1. Locate the following integers on the number line. Then list them in order from smallest to greatest on the line below.

4, 12, −2, 7, −5, 2, −7, 9, −13

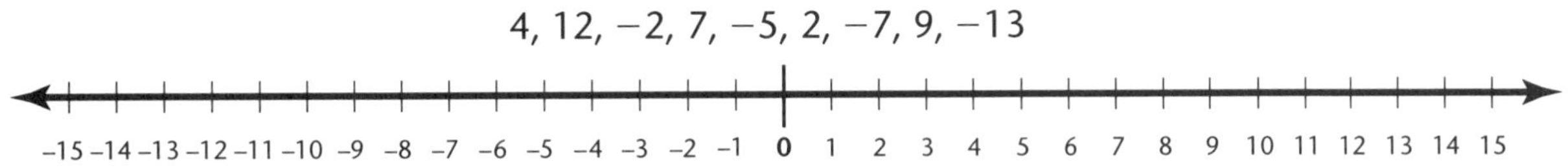

____

2. Use a number line to correctly place the sign > (greater than) or < (less than) between the numbers in each of the following pairs.

a. 89 __________ 98 **b.** −89 __________ −98 **c.** −98 __________ −69

3. This table shows estimates of the mean temperatures on the surface of nine planets. List the planets on the line below in order from hottest to coldest.

Earth	Jupiter	Mars	Mercury	Neptune	Pluto	Saturn	Uranus	Venus
8°C	−150°C	−37°C	179°C	−225°C	−236°C	−185°C	−214°C	453°C

____

Name ______________________ Date ____________ Class ____________

WORKSHEET

10 MATH SKILLS

Arithmetic with Positive and Negative Numbers

The **absolute value** of a number is its distance from zero on the number line. For example, −7 (a negative number) and 7 (a positive number) are the same distance from zero on the number line, and both have an absolute value of 7. Using absolute values simplifies the process of doing arithmetic with positive and negative numbers.

1. Find the absolute value of the following numbers:

a. −7 ______________ **b.** 14 ______________

c. 325,000 ______________ **d.** −475 ______________

e. 230 ______________ **f.** −52 ______________

Part 1: Adding Positive and Negative Numbers

PROCEDURE: Determine if you are adding numbers that have the same or different signs. Then follow the appropriate set of directions below.

Adding same signs	Example −3 + (−5)	Adding opposite signs	Example −3 + 5
Step 1: Add their absolute values.	3 + 5 = 8	**Step 1:** Subtract the smaller absolute value from the larger.	5 − 3 = 2
Step 2: Make the sign of the answer the same as the sign of the original numbers.	Because −3 and −5 are both negative, the answer will be negative. **Answer:** −3 + (−5) = −8	**Step 2:** Choose the sign of the number with the greater absolute value.	Because 5 has a greater absolute value than 3, and 5 is positive, your answer will also be positive. **Answer:** −3 + 5 = 2

Add It Up!

2. Complete the following equations. When finished, go back and check your signs.

a. 14 + (−17) = ______________ **b.** −9 + (−23) = ______________

c. −16 + 21 = ______________ **d.** −12 + 12 = ______________

e. 15 + (−4) = ______________ **f.** −7 + (−7) = ______________

Part 2: Subtracting Positive and Negative Numbers

PROCEDURE: To subtract integers, find the opposite of the number you are subtracting. Then *add* this opposite to the number you are subtracting from. The result is your answer.

SAMPLE PROBLEM: $-3 - (-5) =$ ___?___

Step 1: Find the opposite of the number you want to subtract.

The opposite of -5 is 5.

Step 2: Add this opposite to the number you are subtracting from.

$$-3 - (-5) = -3 + 5 = \mathbf{2}$$

Take It Away!

3. Complete the following subtraction problems. Remember to check your work.

a. $5 - (-7) =$ ______________ **b.** $-11 - 5 =$ ______________

c. $-1 - 1 =$ ______________ **d.** $22 - (-8) =$ ______________

e. $14 - (-3) =$ ______________ **f.** $-9 - 4 =$ ______________

Part 3: Multiplying and Dividing Positive and Negative Numbers

PROCEDURE: To multiply or divide two integers, multiply or divide their absolute values. Then apply the following rule to determine if the answer is positive or negative:

- The product or quotient of two *same-sign* numbers is *positive.*
- The product or quotient of two *opposite-sign* numbers is *negative.*

SAMPLE PROBLEM A: $-7 \times 11 =$ ___?___

Step 1: Multiply the absolute values to find the absolute value of the product.

$$7 \times 11 = 77$$

Step 2: Apply the rule of signs: Because you are finding the product of *opposite-sign* numbers, the product will be *negative.*

$$-7 \times 11 = \mathbf{-77}$$

SAMPLE PROBLEM B: $-12 \div (-4) =$ ___?___

Step 1: Divide the absolute values to find the absolute value of the quotient.

$$12 \div 4 = 3$$

Step 2: Apply the rule of signs: Because you are finding the quotient of *same-sign* numbers, the quotient will be *positive.*

$$-12 \div (-4) = \mathbf{3}$$

Challenge Yourself: Multiply Your Way up the Pyramid!

4. Each brick's number is the product of the two numbers under it. Starting on the bottom row, multiply to complete the empty bricks.

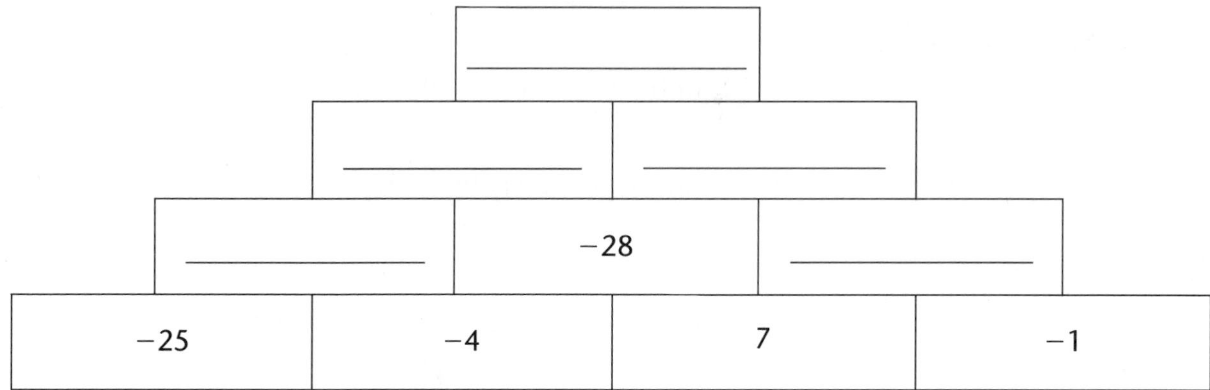

Divide Your Way down Again!

5. Each brick's number is the quotient of the two numbers above it. Starting from the top left brick, divide each brick by the number on its right side. Place the quotient in the empty brick below. Continue until all the bricks are filled.

150,000	−150	____________	3
____________	10	____________	
____________	____________		
______			

Name ______________________ Date ____________ Class ____________

WORKSHEET

11 MATH SKILLS

What Is a Fraction?

Suppose that you are doing an experiment in your class on the benefits of sunlight to plants. Your teacher has asked you to put $\frac{1}{2}$ of the plants in the sun. What does that mean? While whole numbers, such as 1 and 879, are used to indicate *how many,* **fractions** are used to tell *how much of a whole.*

The number below the fraction bar in a fraction is called the *denominator.* This number indicates how many parts there are in the whole. The number above the fraction bar, called the *numerator,* tells you how many parts of that whole are represented.

PROCEDURE: To make a fraction, write the total number of units in the whole as your denominator. Then write the number of parts of that whole being represented as the numerator.

SAMPLE PROBLEM: Your class has 24 plants. Your teacher instructs you to put 5 in a shady spot. What fraction does this represent?

Step 1: Write the total number of parts in the whole as the denominator.

$$\frac{}{24}$$

Step 2: Write the number of parts of the whole being represented as the numerator.

$$\frac{5}{24}$$

$\frac{5}{24}$ of the plants will be in the shade.

Constructing Fractions

1. What fraction of the whole does the shaded or patterned part represent?

a. 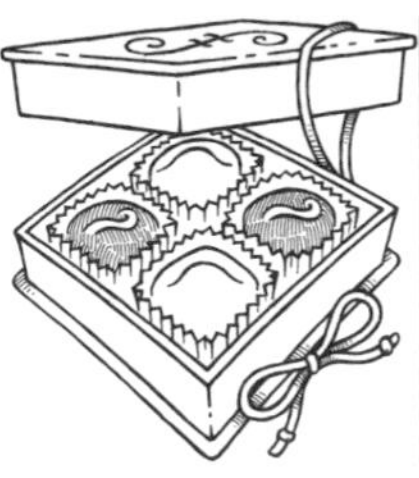 ______

b. 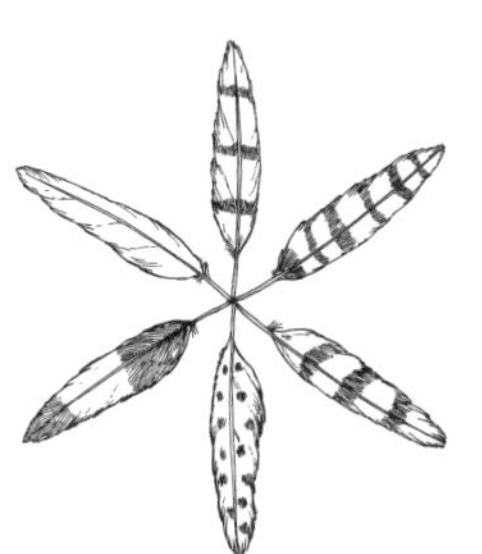 ______

c. 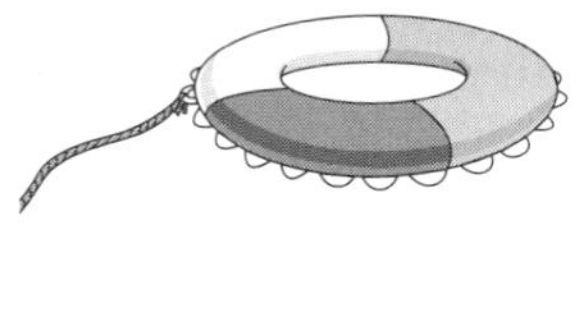 ______

2. Of the 29 students in your class, 10 have brown hair, 8 have black hair, 6 have blond hair, and the rest have red hair.

 a. What fraction of the class has blond hair?

 ____

 b. What fraction of the class has red hair?

 ____

MATH SKILLS

Name ______________________ Date ______________ Class ______________

WORKSHEET

12 MATH SKILLS

Reducing Fractions to Lowest Terms

Suppose you have the fraction $\frac{30}{45}$. Those are pretty big numbers to deal with. Is there a simpler way to write the same fraction? Well, one common method is to write the fraction in **lowest terms.** A fraction in lowest terms is written using the smallest numbers possible that have the same relationship as the numbers in the original fraction. A fraction in lowest terms is the simplest form of that fraction. Read on to learn how to reduce a fraction to lowest terms.

PROCEDURE: To reduce a fraction to lowest terms, first find all the numbers that divide evenly into the numerator and the denominator. These numbers are known as *factors*. Find the largest factor that is common to both the numerator and the denominator. This is known as the **Greatest Common Factor (GCF).** Then divide both the numerator and the denominator by the GCF.

SAMPLE PROBLEM: Reduce the fraction $\frac{30}{45}$ to lowest terms.

Step 1: Find all the factors of the numerator and denominator, and determine which is the largest factor in both lists, or the GCF.

factors of the numerator 30: 1, 2, 3, 5, 6, 10, **15**, 30
factors of the denominator 45: 1, 3, 5, 9, **15**, 45

Step 2: Divide both the numerator and the denominator by the GCF, which is 15.

$$\frac{30}{45} = \frac{30 \div 15}{45 \div 15} = \frac{2}{3}$$

$\frac{30}{45}$ reduced to lowest terms is $\mathbf{\frac{2}{3}}$.

How Low Can You Go?

1. Reduce each fraction to lowest terms.

a. $\frac{10}{12}$ ______ **b.** $\frac{36}{60}$ ______ **c.** $\frac{75}{100}$ ______ **d.** $\frac{17}{68}$ ______

e. $\frac{8}{64}$ ______ **f.** $\frac{48}{54}$ ______ **g.** $\frac{11}{15}$ ______ **h.** $\frac{150}{200}$ ______

2. Circle the fractions below that are already written in lowest terms.

a. $\frac{7}{77}$ **b.** $\frac{21}{25}$ **c.** $\frac{17}{19}$ **d.** $\frac{9}{20}$ **e.** $\frac{37}{51}$

Name ______________________ Date ____________ Class ____________

WORKSHEET

13 **MATH SKILLS**

Improper Fractions and Mixed Numbers

An **improper fraction** is a fraction whose numerator is greater than its denominator, such as $\frac{13}{5}$. An improper fraction can be changed to a **mixed number**, which is a whole number with a fraction, such as $2\frac{3}{5}$. Likewise, a mixed number can be changed to an improper fraction when it is necessary for doing mathematical operations with these numbers.

PROCEDURE: To change an improper fraction to a mixed number, divide the numerator by the denominator and write the quotient as the whole number. If there is a remainder, place it over the denominator to make the fraction of the mixed number.

SAMPLE PROBLEM A: Change $\frac{17}{5}$ to a mixed number.

Step 1: Divide the numerator by the denominator.

$17 \div 5 = 3$, remainder 2

Step 2: Write the quotient as the whole number, and put the remainder over the original denominator as the fraction.

$$\frac{17}{5} = 3\frac{2}{5}$$

PROCEDURE: To change a mixed number to an improper fraction, multiply the denominator of the fraction by the whole number. Then add that product to the numerator. Finally, write the sum over the denominator.

SAMPLE PROBLEM B: Change $4\frac{2}{3}$ to an improper fraction.

Step 1: Multiply the denominator by the whole number.

$3 \times 4 = 12$

Step 2: Add the product to the numerator, and write the sum over the denominator.

$12 + 2 = 14$ $\quad 4\frac{2}{3} = \frac{14}{3}$

1. Write True or False next to each equation.

a. $3\frac{1}{3} = \frac{9}{3}$ ____________ **b.** $\frac{23}{4} = 5\frac{3}{4}$ ____________

c. $\frac{25}{4} = 5\frac{1}{6}$ ____________ **d.** $9\frac{7}{10} = \frac{97}{10}$ ____________

2. Change each improper fraction to a mixed number, and change each mixed number to an improper fraction.

a. $\frac{16}{3} =$ ____________ **b.** $6\frac{1}{3} =$ ____________

c. $3\frac{5}{8} =$ ____________ **d.** $\frac{27}{5} =$ ____________

MATH SKILLS

Name ______________________ Date ____________ Class ____________

WORKSHEET

14 MATH SKILLS

Adding and Subtracting Fractions

Part 1: Adding and Subtracting Fractions with the Same Denominator

PROCEDURE: To add fractions with the same denominator, add the numerators and put the sum over the original denominator. To subtract fractions with the same denominator, subtract the numerators and put the difference over the original denominator.

SAMPLE PROBLEM A:

$$\frac{3}{5} + \frac{1}{5} = ?$$

Add the numerators, and put the sum over the original denominator:

$$\frac{3}{5} + \frac{1}{5} = \frac{3+1}{5} = \frac{4}{5}$$

SAMPLE PROBLEM B:

$$\frac{8}{11} - \frac{3}{11} = ?$$

Subtract the numerators and put the difference over the original denominator:

$$\frac{8}{11} - \frac{3}{11} = \frac{8-3}{11} = \frac{5}{11}$$

Practice What You've Learned!

1. Add and subtract to complete the following equations. Reduce your answers to lowest terms.

a. $\frac{9}{17} - \frac{6}{17} =$ ____________

b. $\frac{5}{24} + \frac{4}{24} =$ ____________

c. $\frac{5}{4} + \frac{3}{4} =$ ____________

d. $\frac{16}{5} - \frac{2}{5} =$ ____________

Part 2: Adding and Subtracting Fractions with Different Denominators

Sometimes you have to add or subtract fractions that have different denominators. To do this, you first need to rewrite your fractions so that they DO have the same denominator. Figuring out the **least common denominator (LCD)** of your fractions is the first step.

PROCEDURE: To find the least common denominator of two fractions, find the least common multiple of the denominators. In other words, look at the multiples of the numbers, and find out which they have in common. The common multiple with the lowest value is your LCD.

SAMPLE PROBLEM: What is the LCD of $\frac{3}{4}$ and $\frac{2}{3}$?

Step 1: List the multiples of 4.

$(4 \times 1) = 4$, $(4 \times 2) = 8$, $(4 \times 3) = \mathbf{12}$, $(4 \times 4) = 16$, etc.

Step 2: List the multiples of 3.

$(3 \times 1) = 3$, $(3 \times 2) = 6$, $(3 \times 3) = 9$, $(3 \times 4) = \mathbf{12}$, etc.

The least common denominator of $\frac{3}{4}$ and $\frac{2}{3}$ is **12.**

Lower Away!

2. Find the least common denominators of the following fractions:

a. $\frac{3}{5}$ and $\frac{5}{4}$ ______

b. $\frac{7}{8}$ and $\frac{4}{3}$ ______

Part 3: Putting the LCD to Work

Now that you know how to find the LCD, you are all set to add and subtract fractions with different denominators. Follow the steps below to see how to use the LCD to add and subtract fractions with different denominators.

PROCEDURE: To add or subtract fractions with different denominators, first find the LCD of the two fractions. Then determine the factor that each denominator is of that LCD. Multiply both the numerator and the denominator by those factors so that the fractions have the same denominator. Then add or subtract the numerators.

SAMPLE PROBLEM: $\frac{1}{2} + \frac{2}{5} = ?$

Step 1: Find the LCD.

$(2 \times 1) = 2$, $(2 \times 2) = 4$, $(2 \times 3) = 6$, $(2 \times 4) = 8$, $(2 \times 5) = \mathbf{10}$, etc.
$(5 \times 1) = 5$, $(5 \times 2) = \mathbf{10}$, etc.
The LCD is **10.**

Step 2: Determine the factor that each denominator is of the LCD.

Because $2 \times \mathbf{5} = 10$, 5 is the factor of 2.
Because $5 \times \mathbf{2} = 10$, **2** is the factor of 5.

Step 3: Multiply the factors of the LCD by the fractions.

$$\frac{1}{2} = \frac{1 \times 5}{2 \times 5} = \frac{5}{10} \qquad \frac{2}{5} = \frac{2 \times 2}{5 \times 2} = \frac{4}{10}$$

Step 4: Add the fractions.

$$\frac{5}{10} + \frac{4}{10} = \mathbf{\frac{9}{10}}$$

Use Your Skills!

3. Add and subtract. Don't forget to reduce your answers to lowest terms.

a. $\frac{2}{9} + \frac{1}{6} =$ ______

b. $\frac{14}{15} - \frac{5}{6} =$ ______

c. $\frac{12}{25} + \frac{2}{5} =$ ______

d. $\frac{1}{2} - \frac{3}{11} =$ ______

▶▶▶ MATH SKILLS

Name ______________________ Date ____________ Class ____________

WORKSHEET

15 **MATH SKILLS**

Multiplying and Dividing Fractions

Compared with adding and subtracting fractions, multiplying and dividing fractions is quite simple. Just follow the steps below to see how it is done.

PROCEDURE 1: *To multiply fractions,* multiply the numerators and the denominators together and reduce the fraction (if necessary).

SAMPLE PROBLEM A: $\frac{5}{9} \times \frac{7}{10} = ?$

Step 1: Multiply the numerators and denominators.	**Step 2:** Reduce.	**Answer:**
$\frac{5}{9} \times \frac{7}{10} = \frac{5 \times 7}{9 \times 10} = \frac{35}{90}$	$\frac{35}{90} = \frac{35 \div 5}{90 \div 5} = \frac{7}{18}$	$\frac{5}{9} \times \frac{7}{10} = \frac{7}{18}$

PROCEDURE 2: *To divide fractions,* switch the numerator and denominator of the divisor (the number you divide by) to make that fraction's *reciprocal.* Then multiply the fraction and the reciprocal, and reduce if necessary.

SAMPLE PROBLEM B: $\frac{5}{8} \div \frac{3}{2} = ?$

Step 1: Rewrite the divisor as its reciprocal.	**Step 2:** Multiply the dividend by the reciprocal.	**Step 3:** Reduce.
$\frac{3}{2} \rightarrow \frac{2}{3}$	$\frac{5}{8} \times \frac{2}{3} = \frac{5 \times 2}{8 \times 3} = \frac{10}{24}$	$\frac{10}{24} = \frac{10 \div 2}{24 \div 2} = \frac{5}{12}$

Practice Your Skills!

1. Multiply and divide to complete the equations. Give your answers in lowest terms.

   a. $\frac{2}{5} \times \frac{5}{6} =$ ______________ b. $\frac{1}{2} \div \frac{3}{8} =$ ______________

   c. $\frac{4}{5} \times \frac{7}{12} =$ ______________ d. $1\frac{1}{2} \div \frac{3}{4} =$ ______________

2. You have $23\frac{1}{4}$ L of saline solution. Every student in the class needs $1\frac{1}{2}$ L for an experiment. How many students can do the experiment?

   ____

   ____

3. Because of differences in gravity, your weight on the moon would be $\frac{1}{6}$ what it is on Earth. If you weigh 72 N, what would be your weight on the moon?

   ____

Name ______________________ Date ____________ Class ____________

WORKSHEET

16 MATH SKILLS

What Is a Ratio?

Imagine that you are planning a science experiment for your class and you want to make sure you have enough beakers for everyone. What do you do? Well, you could simply count the total number of beakers you have and compare it with the number of students in your class. You may not have realized it, but you just made a ratio! A **ratio** is a comparison between numbers, and can be written in words (3 to 7), as a fraction ($\frac{3}{7}$), or with a colon (3:7).

PROCEDURE: To find the ratio between two quantities, show the two quantities as a fraction, and then reduce. The result is the ratio.

SAMPLE PROBLEM: Find the ratio of thermometers to students if you have 36 thermometers and 48 students in your class.

Step 1: Make the ratio. $\frac{36 \text{ thermometers}}{48 \text{ students}}$

Step 2: Reduce. $\frac{36}{48} = \frac{36 \div 12}{48 \div 12} = \frac{3}{4}$

The ratio of thermometers to students is 3 to 4, $\frac{3}{4}$, or 3:4.

Wildflower Research Results

Field	Average number of flowers (per 10 m^2)	Number of species	Species currently flowering
1	51	12	9
2	17	11	7
3	22	22	20

Analyze Your Data!

1. What is the ratio between the currently flowering species and the total number of species of flowers in Field 1?

____

2. What is the ratio between the number of species currently flowering in Field 1 and Field 2 and the number of species currently flowering in Field 3?

____

3. What is the ratio between the number of species currently flowering and the total number of flowers in all three fields?

____

____

Name ______________________ Date ____________ Class ____________

WORKSHEET

17 MATH SKILLS

Using Proportions and Cross-Multiplication

Ratios are a powerful tool in science and math. But in order to take full advantage of them, we have to do more than just calculate ratios—we have to put them to work! For example, if you have three bacteria specimens for every student in your class, you know that you will have a ratio of 3 to 1, $\frac{3}{1}$, or 3:1. But this ratio does not tell you the total number of specimens. To find that, you need to use a proportion.

A **proportion** is a statement of equality between two ratios. This means that the ratios are equal. It also means that the numerator of one ratio multiplied by the denominator of the other ratio is equal to the product of the other numerator and denominator. An example looks like this:

$$\frac{3}{1} \times \frac{12}{4}$$

$$3 \times 4 = 1 \times 12$$

$$12 = 12$$

Notice that you are multiplying across the equal sign in your proportion. This process is called *cross-multiplication.* Cross-multiplication is useful because if you know three of the quantities in a proportion, you can find the fourth.

PROCEDURE: To find an unknown quantity in a proportion, set up the numbers you know in equal ratios. Leave the place for the quantity you do not know empty for now. Then cross-multiply the known numerator of one ratio with the known denominator of the other. Then divide this product by your remaining known quantity. The quotient is your answer.

SAMPLE PROBLEM: Find the missing number in this proportion:

$$\frac{5}{20} = \frac{?}{100}$$

Step 1: Cross-multiply the known numerator of one ratio with the known denominator of the other ratio.

$$\frac{5}{20} \searrow \frac{?}{100} \rightarrow 5 \times 100 = 500$$

Step 2: Divide this product with your remaining known quantity.

$$500 \div 20 = 25$$

The missing number in the proportion is **25;** $\frac{5}{20} = \frac{25}{100}$

Try It Yourself!

1. Find the unknown quantities in the following proportions:

a. $\frac{3}{8} = \frac{?}{24}$ **b.** $\frac{21}{?} = \frac{63}{21}$ **c.** $\frac{?}{3} = \frac{240}{360}$

____________ ____________ ____________

Name ______________________ Date ____________ Class ____________

2. Are the following ratios equal? Show your work and then write Yes or No.

a. $\frac{2}{4} = \frac{10}{30}$ **b.** $\frac{5}{6} = \frac{15}{2}$ **c.** $\frac{2}{5} = \frac{14}{35}$

____________ ____________ ____________

3. A cookie recipe calls for 2 eggs for every 15 cookies. How many eggs will you need to bake 45 cookies? *Hint:* Set up your proportion like the one in the sample problem, leaving the place for the unknown quantity blank.

____

____

4. The ratio of turtles to fish in a pond is 2 to 5.

a. If the pond has 20 fish, how many turtles are there?

____

____

b. How many fish are there if the pond contains 6 turtles?

____

____

Challenge Yourself!

5. In a bird sanctuary, 2 out of every 12 birds are eagles, the ratio of hawks to eagles is 1 to 1, the ratio of woodpeckers to hawks is 1 to 2, and the ratio of hawks to cardinals is 1 to 2.

a. The bird sanctuary also has sparrows. How many birds out of every 12 are sparrows?

____

____

b. How many cardinals are there for every 180 birds?

____

____

Name ______________________ Date ____________ Class ____________

WORKSHEET

18 MATH SKILLS

Decimals and Fractions

Many numbers you will use in science class and other places will be decimal numbers. Like fractions, **decimals** are used to show *how much,* or *what part,* of a whole. A decimal point (.) separates the whole number part of a decimal number on the left from the fraction part on the right. The value of a decimal number is determined by its *place value.* The chart on the right shows the place values for the decimal system. The first place after the decimal point shows parts of ten, or tenths, the second place shows hundredths, and so on. For example, 3.74 is the same as $3 + \frac{7}{10} + \frac{4}{100}$. Any fraction can be changed into a decimal number, and vice versa.

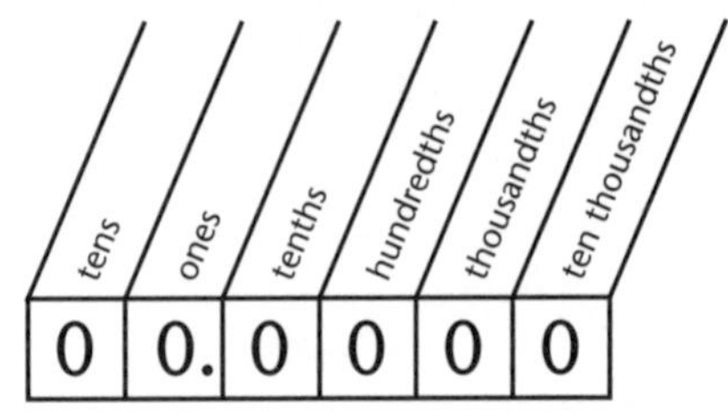

PROCEDURE: *To change a fraction into a decimal,* divide the numerator of the fraction by the denominator. If you have a mixed number (a whole number with a fraction), put the whole-number part of your number before the decimal point.

SAMPLE PROBLEM A: Change $24\frac{3}{20}$ into a decimal number.

Step 1: Divide the numerator of the fraction by the denominator. Notice that 20 does not divide evenly into 3. Therefore, you will need to add zeros after a decimal point in the numerator so that you can divide into it. The answer will be a decimal to show what part of 20 will divide into 3.

$$\begin{array}{r} 0.15 \\ 20\overline{)3.00} \\ -20 \\ \hline 100 \\ -100 \\ \hline 0 \end{array}$$

Step 2: Because $24\frac{3}{20}$ is a mixed number, put the whole number before the decimal point.

$$24\frac{3}{20} = 24.15$$

PROCEDURE: *To change a decimal into a fraction,* put the decimal over its place value and reduce.

SAMPLE PROBLEM B: Convert 0.25 into a fraction. Because 0.25 is in the *hundredths* place, put 25 over 100 and reduce.

$$\frac{25}{100} = \frac{1}{4}$$

1. Change the fractions and mixed numbers into decimal numbers.

a. $\frac{5}{10} =$ ____________ **b.** $7\frac{66}{100} =$ ____________

c. $\frac{15}{25} =$ ____________ **d.** $\frac{165}{55} =$ ____________

2. Convert each decimal number to a fraction or a mixed number.

a. 0.13 = ____________ **b.** 8.405 = ____________

c. 2.98 = ____________ **d.** 0.0001 = ____________

Name ______________________ Date __________ Class __________

WORKSHEET

19 MATH SKILLS

Arithmetic with Decimals

How much would you expect to pay if you were buying a bag of chips for 50 cents and a cola for 75 cents? $1.25, right? Well, if you knew that one, you already know how to add decimals. Doing arithmetic with decimals is a lot like doing arithmetic with whole numbers. Read on to see how it's done.

Part 1: Adding and Subtracting Decimals

PROCEDURE: To add or subtract decimals, line up your numbers vertically so that the decimal points line up. Then add or subtract the columns from right to left, carrying or borrowing numbers when necessary.

SAMPLE PROBLEM: Add the following numbers: 3.1415 and 2.96.

Step1: Line up the numbers vertically so that the decimal points line up.

$$\begin{array}{r} 3.1415 \\ +2.96 \\ \hline \end{array}$$

Step 2: Add the columns from right to left, carrying when necessary.

$$\begin{array}{r} {}^{1\,1} \\ 3.1415 \\ +2.96 \\ \hline 6.1015 \end{array}$$

The sum is **6.1015.**

Do Some Decimal Math!

1. Match the expressions on the left with the letter for their correct answer on the right.

a. 3.2 + 1.9 __________ **A.** 55.11

b. 8.91 − 0.891 __________ **B.** 0.809

c. 50.1 + 5.01 __________ **C.** 5.1

d. 0.999 − 0.19 __________ **D.** 8.019

2. The distance indicator, or odometer, on Robyn's family car reads 32795.2 after a summer vacation. The family drove 631.4 km on the trip. What did the odometer read before the trip?

____

____

3. Sloane has $12 to spend at the hobby shop. Does he have enough money to buy a 5 m rope for $5.64, a bucket of paint for $3.75, and a pack of construction paper for $2.39?

____

____

MATH SKILLS

Part 2: Multiplying Decimal Numbers

PROCEDURE: To multiply decimal numbers, align the numbers vertically and put the number with the most digits on top. Multiply the top number by the bottom number, just like you would multiply whole numbers. Then count the total number of decimal places in both of the multipliers. In your product, move the decimal point to the left the same number of places as there are in the multipliers.

SAMPLE PROBLEM: What is 1.12 × 2.3?

Step 1: Align the numbers vertically, with the longer number on top, and multiply.

$$\begin{array}{r} 1.12 \\ \times\ \ 2.3 \\ \hline 336 \\ 2240 \\ \hline 2576 \end{array}$$

Step 2: Count the total number of decimal places in both numbers being multiplied.

$$\begin{array}{r} 1.12 \\ \times\ \ 2.3 \\ \hline \end{array}$$

There is a total of **3** decimal places.

Step 3: Because there is a total of 3 decimal places in your numbers, move the decimal point in your product 3 places to the *left*.

2576 → 2.576

The product of 1.12 and 2.3 is **2.576.**

Produce Some Products!

4. Calculate the products. Remember to show all your work. If you need more space, use your ScienceLog or a separate sheet of paper.

a. $\begin{array}{r} 0.73 \\ \times\ \ 0.5 \\ \hline \end{array}$

b. $\begin{array}{r} 5.23 \\ \times\ \ 1.9 \\ \hline \end{array}$

c. $\begin{array}{r} 9.12 \\ \times\ \ 8 \\ \hline \end{array}$

d. $\begin{array}{r} 1.12 \\ \times\ \ 0.21 \\ \hline \end{array}$

e. $\begin{array}{r} 90.5 \\ \times\ \ 0.73 \\ \hline \end{array}$

f. $\begin{array}{r} 0.125 \\ \times\ \ 0.3 \\ \hline \end{array}$

5. A typical amoeba is 0.0008 m long. Placed end to end, how long would 150 amoebas be?

____

Challenge Yourself!

6. A hockey player has a career average of 0.9 goals per game during the regular season and 1.6 goals per game in the playoffs. How many goals would you expect him to score in 81 regular season games and 16 playoff games?

____

Part 3: Dividing Decimal Numbers

PROCEDURE: To divide decimal numbers, move the decimal point in the divisor to the right until it is a whole number. Then move the decimal point in the dividend to the right the same number of places. Place a decimal point in the quotient directly above the decimal point in the dividend. Finally, divide as with whole numbers.

SAMPLE PROBLEM: 2.5)8.625

Step 1: Move the decimal point in the divisor to the right until it is a whole number.

2.5)8.625

Step 2: Move the decimal point in the dividend to the right the same number of places, and place a decimal point above it in the quotient.

25)8.6 25

Step 3: Divide as with whole numbers.

```
     3.45
 25)86.25
   -75
    112
   -100
     125
    -125
       0
```

2.5)8.625 = **3.45**

Decimal Division

7. Find the quotients for the following division problems, showing all of your work. If you need more space, use your ScienceLog or a separate piece of paper.

a. 0.2)4.6 ________

b. 0.03)99.6 ________

c. 7)36.4 ________

d. 0.5)95.5 ________

e. 6)240.18 ________

f. 0.4)6.24 ________

8. The snowfall in a year in Peanut Valley was 74.76 cm. What was the average monthly snowfall?

____

9. After constructing a fence around your yard, you calculate that you used 234.5 m of fencing materials. Your yard has a perimeter of 26.8 m. How much fencing material did you use per meter of your yard?

____

____

Name ______________________________ Date ______________ Class ______________

WORKSHEET

20 **MATH SKILLS**

Parts of 100: Calculating Percentages

Let's say you scored 85 percent (%) on your last science test. Does that mean you got 85 questions right? Probably not. The score on your test is expressed as a percentage. The word *percent* comes from Latin words meaning "parts of a 100," and that's exactly what a percentage is. A **percentage** is a ratio that compares a number with 100. Read on to learn how to find a percentage of a number.

PROCEDURE: To find a percentage of a number, first rewrite the percentage you wish to find as a decimal by moving its decimal point two places to the *left*. Then multiply this decimal number by the number you are finding the percentage of. The result is your percentage.

SAMPLE PROBLEM: What is 85% of 40?

Step 1: Rewrite the percentage by moving the decimal point two places to the left.

$$85\% \rightarrow .8.5 \rightarrow 0.85$$

Step 2: Multiply the decimal by the number you are calculating the percentage of.

$$0.85 \times 40 = 34$$

85% of 40 is **34.**

Practice Your Percentages!

1. Calculate the percentages of the following numbers:

a. 30% of 100 ______________ **b.** 90% of 45 ______________

c. 67% of 67 ______________ **d.** 4% of 25 ______________

e. 15% of 225 ______________ **f.** 3.5% of 40 ______________

2. You read in the local paper that the eagle population in Holler State Park has increased 25 percent since 1994. If the population of eagles in 1994 was 28 eagles, how many live in the park now?

____

Challenge Yourself!

3. During a summer drought, a city's water supply is decreased by 35 percent. If the city had a reserve of 45 million liters of water before the drought, how much do they have today?

____

____

Name ______________________ Date __________ Class __________

WORKSHEET

21 **MATH SKILLS**

Percentages, Fractions, and Decimals

Imagine that your science class is doing a school survey to determine which eye colors are most common. The report from the sixth-grade class says that $\frac{3}{5}$ of the students have black or brown eyes, while $\frac{2}{5}$ have blue or green eyes. The seventh-grade class reports that 45 percent have black or brown eyes, and 55 percent have blue or green eyes. The eighth-grade class reports that 0.8 have black or brown eyes, and 0.2 have blue or green eyes. Yikes! Each class has a different way of showing its data! So how do you compare the reports? Well, it's not as complicated as it might look. You see, percentages, fractions, and decimals are just different ways of expressing the same information. Each one tells you *how much* or *how many* of a certain amount. As you learned on the last page, a percentage can be changed to a decimal. For example, 45 percent is equal to 0.45. Percentages can also be changed into fractions. Likewise, every fraction can be expressed as a decimal or percentage, and so on. When comparing numbers or doing operations with numbers, it is often easier to have all of your numbers in the same form before doing calculations.

PROCEDURE 1: To change a fraction to a decimal or percentage, divide the numerator of the fraction by the denominator to make a decimal. To change the decimal number into a percentage, move the decimal point two places to the *right.*

SAMPLE PROBLEM: Change $\frac{3}{5}$ into a decimal number and a percentage.

Step 1: Divide the numerator by the denominator.

$$3 \div 5 = 0.6$$

Step 2: To change the decimal into a percentage, move the decimal point two places to the right.

$$0.6 \rightarrow 0.60 \rightarrow \mathbf{60\%}$$

PROCEDURE 2: To change a decimal number into a fraction or percentage, place the decimal over its place value and reduce. To change a decimal into a percentage, see Step 2 of Procedure 1.

SAMPLE PROBLEM: Express 0.56 as a fraction and a percentage.

Step 1: Because 0.56 is in the *hundredths* place, put the whole number over 100 and reduce.

$$\frac{56}{100} = \frac{14}{25}$$

Step 2: To change a decimal into a percentage, move the decimal point two places to the right, as in step 2 of procedure 1.

$$0.56 \rightarrow 0.56 \rightarrow 56\%$$

Practice What You've Learned

1. Express the following percentages as decimal numbers:

a. 52% ____________ **b.** 99% ____________

c. 7.8% ____________ **d.** 0.57% ____________

▶▶▶ MATH SKILLS

2. Express the following fractions as both a decimal number and a percentage.

a. $\frac{75}{100} =$ ______________ **b.** $\frac{1}{8} =$ ______________

c. $\frac{9}{20} =$ ______________ **d.** $\frac{12}{4} =$ ______________

e. $\frac{26}{13} =$ ______________ **f.** $\frac{8}{32} =$ ______________

3. Change the following decimal numbers into both a fraction and a percentage:

a. 0.3 = ______________ **b.** 0.12 = ______________

c. 0.99 = ______________ **d.** 1.5 = ______________

e. 0.505 = ______________ **f.** 0.01 = ______________

4. Write True or False next to each equation.

a. $2\frac{2}{5} = 2.4 = 24\%$ ______________

b. $0.03 = 3\% = \frac{3}{100}$ ______________

c. $0.45\% = \frac{90}{200} = 0.0045$ ______________

d. $5.25 = 5\frac{14}{28} = 525\%$ ______________

5. Convert the following equations into the same form and calculate. Hint: Do the calculation inside the parentheses before adding or subtracting.

a. $\frac{2}{5} + 0.12 =$ ______________

b. $(75\% \text{ of } 60) - 3\frac{3}{5} =$ ______________

c. $\frac{32}{8} - (15\% \text{ of } 20) =$ ______________

Name ______________________ Date ____________ Class ____________

WORKSHEET

22 **MATH SKILLS**

Working with Percentages and Proportions

When working with percentages, it is often helpful to think of them in terms of ratios and proportions. For instance, if someone asks you, "What is 10% of 40?" you could simply change 10% into a decimal (0.1) and multiply it by 40 to get 4. But what if you were asked, "5% of what number is 10?" That's a little trickier. To do this calculation, it is convenient to use a proportion.

PROCEDURE: To use percentages in a proportion, first put your known percentage in a ratio with 100. Then create an equivalent ratio, leaving the place for your unknown quantity blank. Cross-multiply the known numerator with the known denominator. Divide the product with your remaining known value. The result is your unknown quantity.

SAMPLE PROBLEM: 25% of what number is 4?

Step 1: Put your percentage in a ratio with 100. $\frac{25}{100}$	**Step 2:** Create an equivalent ratio, leaving the space for the unknown quantity blank. $\frac{25}{100} = \frac{4}{?}$
Step 3: Cross-multiply the known numerator with the known denominator. $\frac{25}{100} \swarrow\!\!\nearrow \frac{4}{?} \rightarrow 100 \times 4 = 400$	**Step 4:** Divide the product with the remaining known quantity. $400 \div 25 = 16$

25% of **16** is 4.

Figure It Out!

1. Follow the steps above to answer the following questions:

   a. 15% of what number is 3? ____________

   b. 25% of what number is 11? ____________

   c. 8% of what number is 4? ____________

   d. 24% of what number is 168? ____________

2. A biologist estimates that the number of frogs living in Lasso Pond increased last summer by about 70 frogs. If this represents a 25 percent increase, how many frogs lived in the pond before last summer?

____

____

MATH SKILLS

Name ______________________ Date ______________ Class ______________

WORKSHEET

23 MATH SKILLS

Counting the Zeros

A **power of 10** is a number that can have 10 as its only factors. For instance, $(10 \times 10) = $ *100* and $(10 \times 10 \times 10 \times 10) = $ *10,000* are both powers of 10. Multiplying and dividing by powers of 10 is as easy as counting the zeros and moving your decimal point the same number of places.

Part 1: Multiplying by Powers of 10

PROCEDURE: To multiply a number by a power of 10, move the decimal point to the *right* the same number of places as there are zeros in the power of 10. If there are not enough places in your number to do this, you will need to add zeros to the number as place holders.

SAMPLE PROBLEM: Multiply 8.25 by 10, 100, and 1000.

$$\mathbf{10} \times 8.25 = 8.2\,5 \rightarrow 82.5$$
$$\mathbf{100} \times 8.25 = 8.2\,5 \rightarrow 825$$
$$\mathbf{1000} \times 8.25 = 8.2\,5\,0 \rightarrow 8250$$

It's Your Turn!

1. Write your answers on the lines, and remember to place commas in the appropriate places.

a. $10 \times 6 = $ ______________ **b.** $9.381 \times 100 = $ ______________

c. $71 \times 100 = $ ______________ **d.** $1000 \times 41 = $ ______________

e. $10 \times 11.9 = $ ______________ **f.** $67 \times 10{,}000 = $ ______________

Part 2: Dividing by Powers of 10

PROCEDURE: To divide a number by a power of 10, move the decimal point to the left as many places as there are zeros in the power of 10.

SAMPLE PROBLEM: Divide 763 by 10, 1000, and 100,000.

$$763 \div \mathbf{10} = 76\,3 \rightarrow 76.3$$
$$763 \div \mathbf{1000} = 7\,6\,3 \rightarrow 0.763$$
$$763 \div \mathbf{100{,}000} = 0\,0\,7\,6\,3 \rightarrow 0.00763$$

2. Divide by powers of 10.

a. $55 \div 1000 = $ ______________ **b.** $9907 \div 100 = $ ______________

c. $620 \div 10 = $ ______________ **d.** $4.01 \div 100 = $ ______________

e. $0.04 \div 1000 = $ ______________ **f.** $996 \div 10{,}000 = $ ______________

Name ______________________ Date ____________ Class ____________

WORKSHEET

24 MATH SKILLS

Creating Exponents

Imagine that you are writing a paper for your science class and need to write many very large numbers, such as 10,000,000,000,000. Your fingers would get pretty tired writing all those zeros. However, there is a simpler way to express these large powers of 10. An **exponent** is a small number placed above and to the right of a base number to show how many times the base number is multiplied by itself. For example, 100,000 is 10 multiplied by itself five times, or $10 \times 10 \times 10 \times 10 \times 10$. Written in exponential form, 100,000 is 10^5. The exponent number tells you how many zeros are in your power of 10.

PROCEDURE: To change a power of 10 into exponential form, first count the number of zeros in your power of 10. This number will be your exponent. Place the exponent above and to the right of the base number of 10.

SAMPLE PROBLEM: Write 10,000,000,000,000 in exponential form.

Step 1: Count the zeros in your power of 10.

10,000,000,000,000 has 13 zeros.

Step 2: Place your exponent above and to the right of your base number 10.

10^{13}

10,000,000,000,000 = $\mathbf{10^{13}}$

On Your Own!

1. Convert the following powers of 10 into exponential form:

   a. 1000 = ____________ b. 10,000,000 = ____________

   c. 1,000,000 = ____________ d. 10,000,000,000 = ____________

   e. 10,000,000,000,000,000,000,000,000,000,000,000,000 = ____________

2. Change the following exponent numbers into powers of 10:

   a. 10^5 = ____________ b. 10^2 = ____________

   c. 10^9 = ____________ d. 10^{12} = ____________

   e. 10^{29} = ____________

MATH SKILLS

Name ______________________ Date ____________ Class ____________

WORKSHEET

25 MATH SKILLS

What Is Scientific Notation?

Sometimes scientific calculations result in very large numbers, like 918,700,000,000,000, or in very small numbers, such as 0.0000000578. **Scientific notation** is a short way of representing such numbers without writing the place-holding zeros. In scientific notation, we write the number as a product of two factors: the first is a number between 1 and 10, and the second is a power of ten, written as 10^{exponent}.

PROCEDURE: To write a number in scientific notation, first identify which digits are not place-holding zeros. Then place the decimal point after the leftmost digit. To find the exponent for the factor of 10, count the number of places that you moved the decimal point. If you moved the decimal point to the left, the exponent will be positive. If you moved the decimal point to the right, the exponent will be negative.

SAMPLE PROBLEM: Write 653,000,000 in scientific notation.

Step 1: Identify the number without the place-holding zeros.

653

Step 2: Place the decimal point after the leftmost digit.

6.53

Step 3: Find the exponent by counting the number of places that you moved the decimal point.

6,5,3,,0,0,0,,0,0,0 → 6.53

The decimal point was moved 8 places to the left. Therefore, the exponent of 10 is positive 8. *Remember*, if the decimal point had moved to the right, the exponent would be negative.

Step 4: Write the number in scientific notation.

$\mathbf{6.53 \times 10^{8}}$

Practice Your Skills!

Original number	Number without place-holding zeros	Power of 10	Number in scientific notation
1. 530,000			
2. 904,580,000			
3. 0.000000617			

4. Express the following data in scientific notation:

a. 53,657 kg ____________ **b.** 0.000043 L ____________

c. 0.00083 m ____________ **d.** 1011.9 cm ____________

Name ____________________ Date __________ Class __________

WORKSHEET

26 MATH SKILLS

Multiplying and Dividing in Scientific Notation

Part 1: Multiplying in Scientific Notation

PROCEDURE: To multiply numbers in scientific notation, multiply the decimal numbers. Then *add* the exponents of the powers of 10. Place the new power of 10 with the decimal in scientific notation form. If your decimal number is greater than 10, count the number of times the decimal moves to the left, and add this number to the exponent.

SAMPLE PROBLEM: Multiply (2.6×10^7) by (6.3×10^4).

Step 1: Multiply the decimal numbers. $2.6 \times 6.3 = 16.38$	**Step 2:** Add the exponents. $7 + 4 = 11$
Step 3: Put the new decimal number with the new exponent in scientific notation form. 16.38×10^{11}	**Step 4:** Because the new decimal number is greater than 10, count the number of places the decimal moves to put the number between 1 and 10. Add this number to the exponent. In this case, the decimal point moves one place, so add 1 to the exponent. $16.38 \times 10^{11} \rightarrow 1.638 \times 10^{12}$

Try It Yourself!

1. Follow the steps in the Sample Problem carefully to complete the following equations.

Multiplying with Scientific Notations

Problem	New decimal	New exponent	Answer
Sample problem: $(4.4 \times 10^6) \times (3.9 \times 10^4)$	$4.4 \times 3.9 = 17.16$	$6 + 4 = 10$	1.716×10^{11}
a. $(2.8 \times 10^8) \times (1.9 \times 10^4)$			
b. $(1.3 \times 10^9) \times (4.7 \times 10^{-5})$			
c. $(3.7 \times 10^{15}) \times (5.2 \times 10^7)$			
d. $(4.9 \times 10^{24}) \times (1.6 \times 10^5)$			

2. The mass of one hydrogen atom is 1.67×10^{-27} kg. A cylinder contains 3.01×10^{23} hydrogen atoms. What is the mass of the hydrogen?

____

MATH SKILLS

Part 2: Dividing in Scientific Notation

PROCEDURE: To divide numbers in scientific notation, first divide the decimal numbers. Then *subtract* the exponents of your power of 10. Place the new power of 10 with the decimal in scientific notation form. If the resulting decimal number is less than 1, move the decimal point to the right and decrease the exponent by the number of places that the decimal point moved.

SAMPLE PROBLEM: Divide (1.23×10^{11}) by (2.4×10^{4}).

Step 1: Divide the decimal numbers.	**Step 2:** Subtract the exponents of the powers of 10.
$1.23 \div 2.4 = 0.5125$	$11 - 4 = 7$
Step 3: Place the new power of 10 with the new decimal in scientific notation form.	**Step 4:** Because the decimal number is not between 1 and 10, move the decimal point one place to the right and decrease the exponent by 1.
0.5125×10^{7}	$0.5125 \times 10^{7} \rightarrow 5.125 \times 10^{6}$

$(1.23 \times 10^{11}) \div (2.4 \times 10^{4}) = \mathbf{5.125 \times 10^{6}}$

3. Complete the following chart:

Dividing with Scientific Notation

Problem	New decimal	New exponent	Answer
Sample problem: $(5.76 \times 10^{9}) \div (3.2 \div 10^{3})$	$5.76 \div 3.2 = 1.8$	$9 - 3 = 6$	1.8×10^{6}
a. $(3.72 \times 10^{8}) \div (1.2 \times 10^{5})$			
b. $(6.4 \times 10^{-4}) \div (4 \times 10^{6})$			
c. $(3.6 \times 10^{4}) \div (6 \times 10^{5})$			
d. $(1.44 \times 10^{24}) \div (1.2 \times 10^{17})$			

4. The average distance from Earth to the sun is 1.5×10^{11} m. The speed of light is 3×10^{8} m/s. Approximately how long does it take for light to travel from the sun to Earth?

____

____

Name ______________________ Date ____________ Class ____________

WORKSHEET

27 MATH SKILLS

What Is SI?

To make sharing information easier, most of the world uses the SI of measurement. **SI,** which stands for *Système Internationale d'Unités,* is a standard for measuring mass, length, volume, and other quantities. It is used by all scientists to avoid the confusion of comparing data that is based on different measuring systems. Three common SI units are in the chart at right. Obviously, these three units are not suitable for all measuring needs. But most quantities can be measured using one of these units with one of the prefixes in the chart below.

Quantity	Unit	Symbol
length	meter	m
volume	liter	L
mass	gram	g

Prefix	Powers of 10	Symbol	Example
kilo-	1000 (10^3)	k	kilogram (kg)
hecto-	100 (10^2)	h	hectoliter (hL)
deca-	10 (10^1)	da	decameter (dam)
—	1	—	meter (m), gram (g), liter (L)
deci-	0.1 (10^{-1})	d	decigram (dg)
centi-	0.01 (10^{-2})	c	centimeter (cm)
milli-	0.001 (10^{-3})	m	milliliter (mL)

PROCEDURE: To convert between SI units, first find the prefixes of your numbers in the chart above. If you are converting from a smaller prefix to a larger prefix (moving *up* the chart), *divide* your number by a power of 10. If you are converting from a larger prefix to a smaller prefix (moving *down* the chart), *multiply* your number by a power of 10.

SAMPLE PROBLEM A: Convert 500 decimeters (dm) to kilometers (km).

Step 1: Find the prefixes of the numbers.

decimeters to **kilo**meters

Step 2: Notice that you will move up the chart four places when converting from deci- to kilo-. Therefore, you will *divide* your number by $10 \times 10 \times 10 \times 10$, or 10,000.

$500 \div 10{,}000 = 0500 \rightarrow 0.05$

500 decimeters (dm) = **0.05 kilometers** (km)

SAMPLE PROBLEM B: 2.5 centiliters (cL) is how many milliliters (mL)?

Step 1: Find the prefixes.

centiliters to **milli**liters

Step 2: Because you move down the chart one place when converting from centi- to milli-, multiply your number by 10.

$2.5 \times 10 = 2.5 \rightarrow 25$

2.5 centiliters (cL) = **25 milliliters** (mL)

MATH SKILLS

Work with the System!

1. Write True or False next to each statement.

a. 12 hg = 1.2 kg __________ **b.** 54 cm = 5.4 mm __________

c. 0.5 dL = 0.005 cL __________ **d.** 4.5 g = 0.45 dag __________

e. 111 cm = 1.11 m __________ **f.** 7 cL = 70,000 kL __________

2. Fill in the missing numbers and units in the equations below.

a. 25 mm = __________ cm **b.** 27 kg = 270,000 ______

c. 50 cm = 0.005 ______ **d.** 1.2 dL = __________ L

e. 0.9 L= __________ mL **f.** 41 hm = 4,100,000 ______

3. 1 m = __________ dm = __________ cm = __________ mm

4. 5 kg = __________ hg = __________ dg = __________ cg

5. Special balances can weigh to the 0.00000001 g. How many kilograms is this?

____

6. A chemistry experiment calls for 5 g of baking soda. Your measuring spoon holds 5000 mg of powder. How many scoops will you need for the experiment?

____

Challenge Yourself!

Some SI prefixes are almost never used because they are so small or large. A micrometer (μm) is 10^{-6} m, while a nanometer is 10^{-9} m. A gigameter is 10^{9} m.

7. a. How many nanometers are in 1 gigameter?

____

b. How many gigameters are in 1,000,000,000,000 micrometers?

____

Name ______________________ Date __________ Class __________

WORKSHEET

28 MATH SKILLS

A Formula for SI Catch-up

Scientists use SI all the time. But most people in the United States still use non-SI units. So what do you do if you have data in non-SI units and you want to convert the data into SI units, or vice versa? Have no fear! Conversion charts, like the one shown below, can help you accomplish the task with ease.

SI Conversion Chart

If you know	Multiply by	To find
inches (in.)	2.54	centimeters (cm)
feet (ft)	30.50	centimeters (cm)
yards (yd)	0.91	meters (m)
miles (mi)	1.61	kilometers (km)
ounces (oz)	28.35	grams (g)
pounds (lb)	0.45	kilograms (kg)
fluid ounces (fl oz)	29.57	milliliters (mL)
cups (c)	0.24	liters (L)
pints (pt)	0.47	liters (L)
quarts (qt)	0.94	liters (L)
gallons (gal)	3.79	liters (L)

PROCEDURE: *To convert from non-SI units to SI units,* find the non-SI unit in the left column and multiply it by the number in the center column. The resulting number will be in the SI unit in the right column.

To convert a SI unit into a non-SI unit, find the SI unit in the right column and divide by the number in the center column to get the non-SI unit on the left.

SAMPLE PROBLEM: Convert 15 gal into liters (L).

$15 \times 3.79 =$ **56.85 L**

Complete the Conversions!

1. Use the SI conversion chart to do the following conversions (round to the nearest hundredths):

a. 15 oz = ______________ g **b.** 40 cm = ______________ in.

c. 2 c = ______________ L **d.** 27 m = ______________ yd

e. 5.5 gal = ______________ L **f.** 115 lb = ______________ kg

MATH SKILLS

2. A chemistry experiment calls for 6 mL of HCl (hydrochloric acid). How many fluid ounces is this?

____

3. Simone wants to compete in a 15 km run. The farthest she can run is 10 mi. Can she finish the race?

____

____

4. A cake recipe calls for 1 cup of milk. How many milliliters is this?

____

5. Julie is 162 cm tall. How tall is she in feet?

____

6. George ran 1000 yd in gym class. How many kilometers did he run?

____

____

7. Alejandro weighed 8 lb, 4 oz when he was born. How many grams did he weigh?

____

____

____

Name ______________________ Date ____________ Class ____________

WORKSHEET

29 **MATH SKILLS**

Finding Perimeter and Area

Suppose your class has been asked to build a garden for your school. In order to keep the garden clean and undisturbed, your class decides to build a fence around the outside of it. How much fencing material will you need? The answer to this question can be found with geometry. The distance around the outside of any figure is called the **perimeter** *(P)*. In the case of the garden, the perimeter will equal the total length of the fence.

Part 1: Calculating Perimeter

PROCEDURE: To find the perimeter of a figure, add the lengths of all the sides.

SAMPLE PROBLEM: Find the perimeter *(P)* of the figure.

$$9 + 5 + 4 + 7 + 10 + 4 + 5 + 8 = 52$$

$$P = \mathbf{52\ m}$$

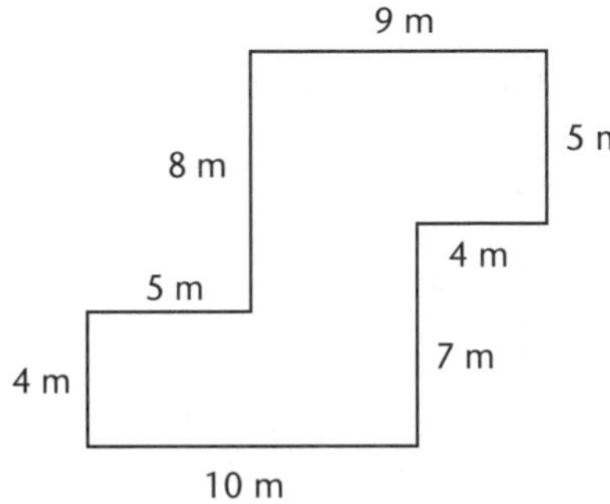

1. Using a metric ruler, measure the sides of the figures below in centimeters, and calculate the perimeter of each figure.

a.

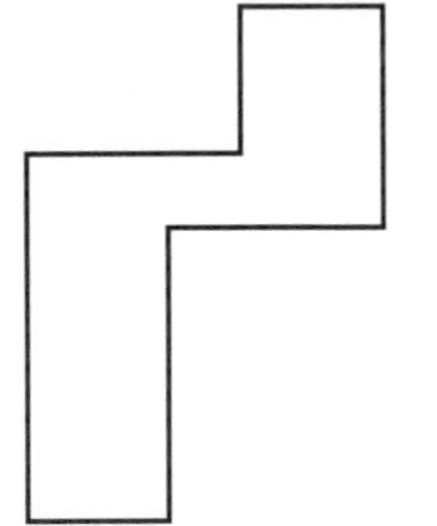

$P =$ ____________

b.

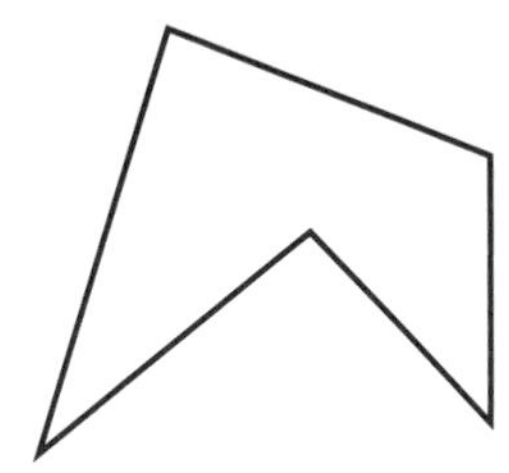

$P =$ ____________

c.

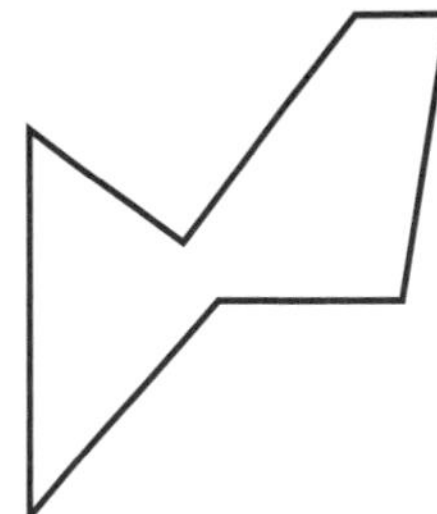

$P =$ ____________

2. Use the lengths to determine the perimeter of the figures.

a. Rectangle: length = 4m
width = 2m

$P =$ ____________

b. Square: side = 45 mm

$P =$ ____________

c. Equilateral triangle: side = 6 m

$P =$ ____________

d. Rectangle: length = 3.5 cm
width = 2.4 cm

$P =$ ____________

MATH SKILLS

Part 2: Calculating Area

Now that you know how to find the perimeter of the garden, you are ready to plan what to grow. How much planting soil will you need? How many plants will fit in the garden? To answer these questions, you will need to know the area of the garden. **Area** (*A*) is the number of square units needed to cover the surface of a figure. The equations below will help you find the area of some common figures.

EQUATIONS: Area of a square = side × side

Area of a rectangle = length × width

Area of a triangle = $\frac{1}{2}$ × base × height

SAMPLE PROBLEMS: Find the area (*A*) of each of the following figures:

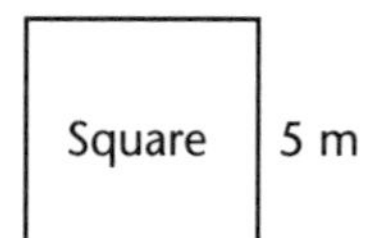

A = side × side

$A = 5 \text{ m} \times 5 \text{ m}$

$A = \mathbf{25\ m^2}$

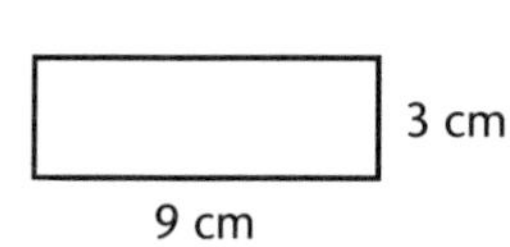

A = length × width

$A = 9 \text{ cm} \times 3 \text{ cm}$

$A = \mathbf{27\ cm^2}$

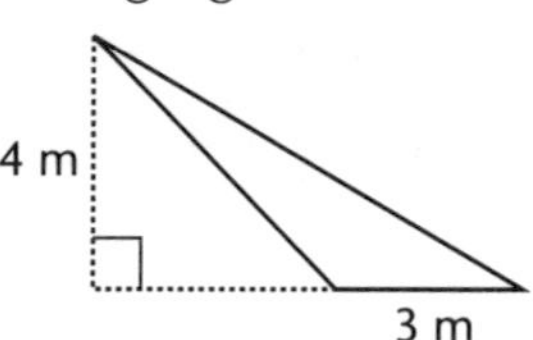

$A = \frac{1}{2}$ × base × height

$A = \frac{1}{2} \times 3 \text{ m} \times 4 \text{ m}$

$A = \mathbf{6\ m^2}$

Area Alert!

3. Find the area of each figure below. *Hint:* When finding the area of irregular figures, first divide the figures up into triangles, squares, and rectangles and then add their individual areas.

a.

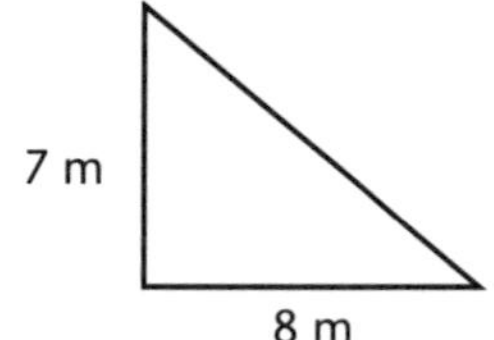

A = ______________

b.

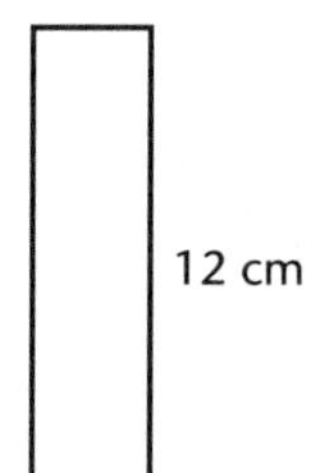

A = ______________

c.

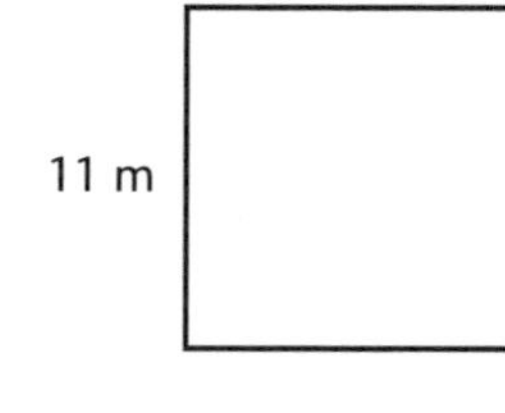

A = ______________

d.

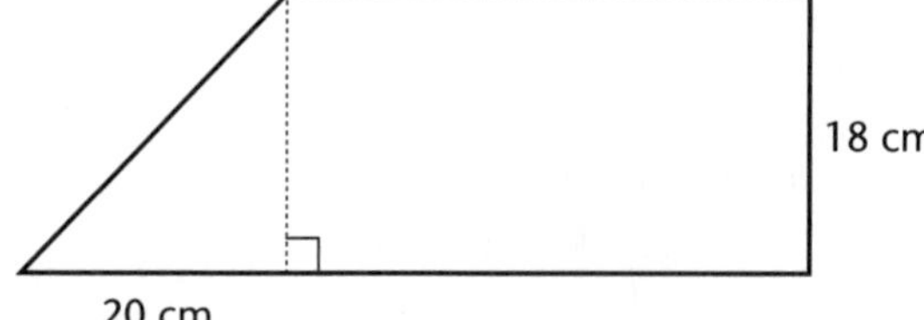

A = ______________

e.

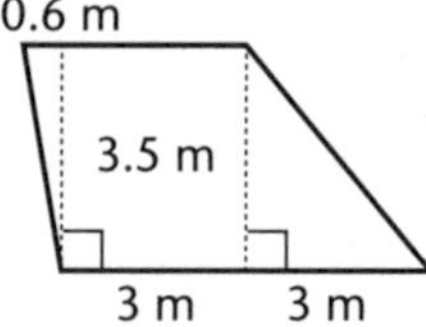

A = ______________

Name ______________________ Date __________ Class __________

WORKSHEET

30 **MATH SKILLS**

Finding Volume

Volume (V) is the amount of space something occupies. It is expressed in cubic units, such as cubic meters (m^3) and cubic centimeters (cm^3). Use the equations for volume below to calculate the volume of cubes and prisms.

EQUATIONS: Volume of a cube = side × side × side
Volume of a prism = area of base × height

SAMPLE PROBLEMS: Find the volume (V) of the solids.

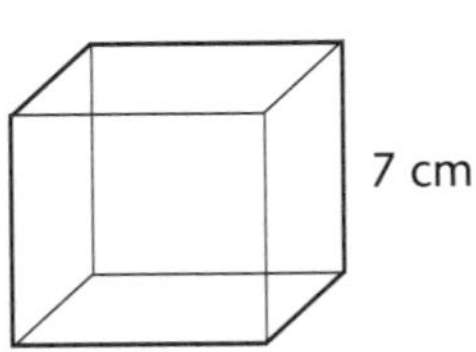

V = side × side × side
V = 7 cm × 7 cm × 7 cm
V = **343 cm³**

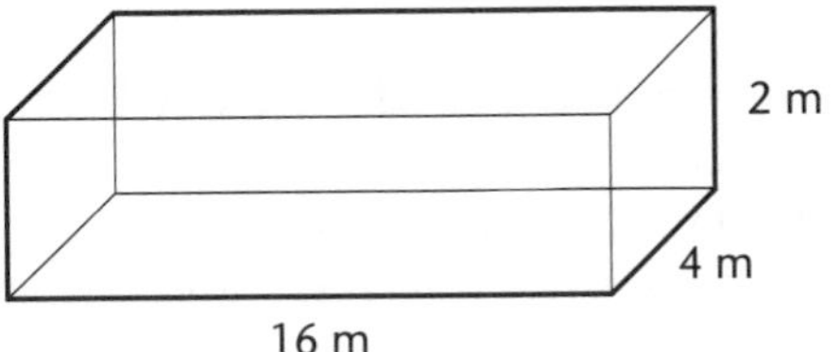

V = area of base × height
V = (length × width) × height
V = (16 m × 4 m) × 2 m
V = 64 m² × 2 m
V = **128 m³**

Turn Up the Volume!

1. Find the volume of the solids.

a.

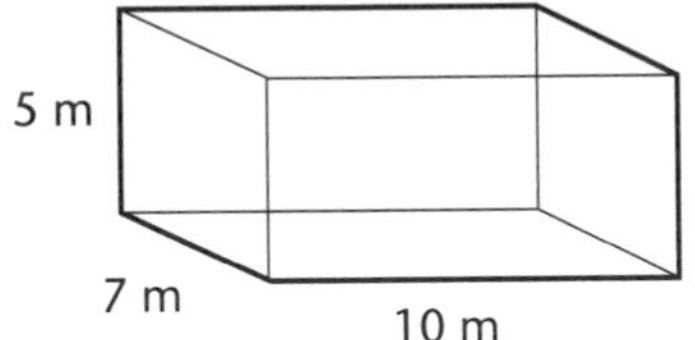

V = ______________________

b.

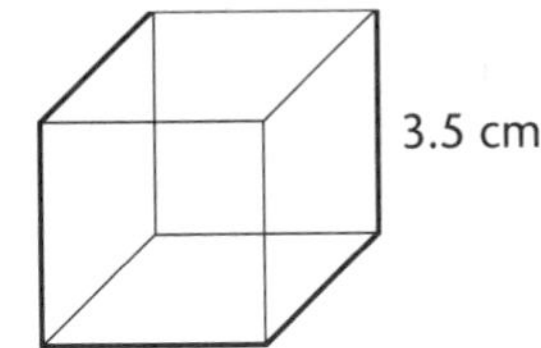

V = ______________________

c.

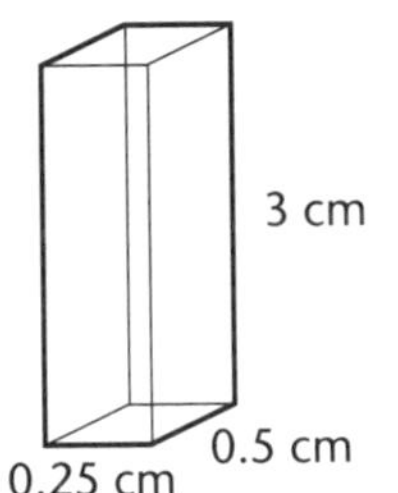

V = ______________________

d.

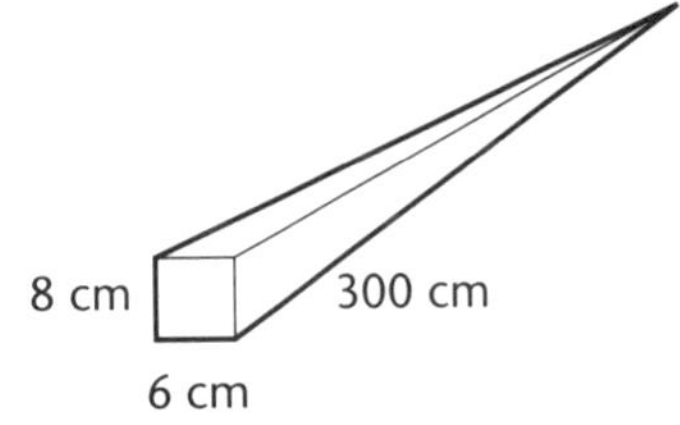

V = ______________________

Challenge Yourself!

2. A rectangular-shaped swimming pool is 50 m long and 2.5 m deep and holds 2500 m³ of water. What is the width of the pool?

____

Name ______________________ Date ______________ Class ____________

WORKSHEET

31 MATH SKILLS

The Unit Factor and Dimensional Analysis

The measurements you take in science class, whether for time, mass, weight, or distance, are more than just numbers—they are also units. To make comparisons between measurements, it is convenient to have your measurements in the same units. A mathematical tool called a **unit factor** is used to convert back and forth between different kinds of units. A unit factor is a ratio that is equal to 1. Because it is equal to 1, multiplying a measurement by a unit factor changes the measurement's units but does not change its value. The skill of converting with a unit factor is known as **dimensional analysis.** Read on to see how it works.

Part 1: Converting with a Unit Factor

PROCEDURE: To convert units with a unit factor, determine the conversion factor between the units you have and the units you want to convert to. Then create the unit factor by making a ratio, in the form of a fraction, between the units you want to convert to in the numerator and the units you already have in the denominator. Finally, multiply your measurement by this unit factor to convert to the new units.

SAMPLE PROBLEM A: Convert 3.5 km to millimeters.

Step 1: Determine the conversion factor between kilometers and millimeters.

$$1 \text{ km} = 1{,}000{,}000 \text{ mm}$$

Step 2: Create the unit factor. Put the units you want to convert to in the numerator and the units you already have in the denominator.

$$\frac{1{,}000{,}000 \text{ mm}}{1 \text{ km}} = 1$$

Step 3: Multiply the unit factor by the measurement. Notice that the original unit of the measurement cancels out with the unit in the denominator of the unit factor, leaving the units you are converting to.

$$3.5 \cancel{\text{km}} \times \frac{1{,}000{,}000 \text{ mm}}{1 \cancel{\text{km}}} = \mathbf{3{,}500{,}000 \text{ mm}}$$

On Your Own!

1. Convert the following measurements using a unit factor:

Conversion	Unit factor	Answer
a. 2.34 cm = ? mm		
b. 54.6 mL = ? L		
c. 12 kg = ? g		

Part 2: Working with Square Units

Many times in your science class, you will work with units of two dimensions, such as square centimeters (cm^2) or square kilometers (km^2). Dimensional analysis is especially useful when working with these types of units because it can help you to avoid confusing the different dimensions of your units. Carefully follow the steps in Sample Problem B to see how it works.

SAMPLE PROBLEM B: 1 km^2 is how many square meters?

Step 1: Simplify the units you are converting.

$$1 \text{ km}^2 = 1 \text{ km} \times 1 \text{ km}$$

Step 2: Create the unit factor for converting meters to kilometers. As in Sample Problem A, put the units you are converting *to* in the numerator.

$$\frac{1000 \text{ m}}{1 \text{ km}} = 1$$

Step 3: Multiply the measurement you are converting by the unit factor. Because 1 km^2 = 1 km × 1 km, you will need to multiply the measurement you are converting from by *two* unit factors. Notice that the original unit of measurement cancels the units in the denominator. This leaves the units you are converting *to*.

$$1 \cancel{\text{km}^2} \times \frac{1000 \text{ m}}{1 \cancel{\text{km}}} \times \frac{1000 \text{ m}}{1 \cancel{\text{km}}} = 1{,}000{,}000 \text{ m} \times \text{m}$$

$$1 \text{ km}^2 = \mathbf{1{,}000{,}000 \text{ m}^2}$$

Practice Your Skills!

2. Convert the following measurements:

Conversion	Unit factor	Answer
a. 3 cm^2 = ? m^2		
b. 12,000 m^2 = ? km^2		
c. 980 cm^2 = ? mm^2		

3. An Olympic-sized soccer field has an area of 0.007776 km^2. How many square meters does a soccer field cover?

____

____

Working with Cubic Dimensions

Because volume can be measured by multiplying length times height times width, volume is expressed in units of three dimensions, or cubic units. Volume is often expressed in cubic millimeters (mm^3) or cubic centimeters (cm^3), but larger volumes may be expressed in cubic meters (m^3) or cubic kilometers (km^3). A cubic centimeter (cm^3) is equal to one milliliter (mL), and a cubic decimeter (dm^3) is equal to one liter (L). Doing dimensional analysis with cubic units is much like doing dimensional analysis with square units, except that with cubic units you will multiply the measurement you are converting by three unit factors instead of two. Follow the steps in Sample Problem C to see how it is done.

SAMPLE PROBLEM C: A certain plant needs about 525 cm^3 of soil to grow properly. How many cubic meters of soil is this?

Step 1: Simplify the units you are converting.

$$cm^3 = cm \times cm \times cm$$

Step 2: Create the unit factor for converting centimeters to meters, putting the units you are converting *to* in the numerator.

$$\frac{1\ m}{100\ cm}$$

Step 3: Multiply the measurement you are converting by the unit factors. Because $cm^3 = cm \times cm \times cm$, you will need to multiply the measurement you are converting from by *three* unit factors.

$$525\ \cancel{cm}^3 \times \frac{1\ m}{100\ \cancel{cm}} \times \frac{1\ m}{100\ \cancel{cm}} \times \frac{1\ m}{100\ \cancel{cm}} = 0.000525\ m \times m \times m$$

$$525\ cm^3 = \mathbf{0.000525\ m^3}$$

Try It Yourself!

4. Convert the following measurements:

Conversion	Unit factor	Answer
a. 30 m^3 = ? cm^3		
b. 9000 mm^3 = ? m^3		
c. 4 km^3 = ? m^3		

Challenge Yourself!

5. The Mississippi River has an average water discharge of 17,000 m^3 per second. How many cubic kilometers of water does the river discharge in 1 hour? Show your work.

______

______

______

Name ______________________ Date ____________ Class ____________

WORKSHEET

32 MATH IN SCIENCE: INTEGRATED SCIENCE

MATH SKILLS USED
Multiplication Division Decimals

Density

Calculate density, and identify substances using a density chart.

Density is a measure of the amount of mass in a certain volume. This physical property is often used to identify and classify substances. It is usually expressed in grams per cubic centimeters, or g/cm³. The chart on the right lists the densities of some common materials.

Densities of Substances

Substance	Density (g/cm³)
Gold	19.3
Mercury	13.5
Lead	11.4
Iron	7.87
Aluminum	2.7
Bone	1.7–2.0
Gasoline	0.66–0.69
Air (dry)	0.00119

EQUATION: $\text{density} = \frac{\text{mass}}{\text{volume}}$

$$D = \frac{m}{V}$$

SAMPLE PROBLEM: What is the density of a billiard ball that has a volume of 100 cm³ and a mass of 250 g?

$$D = \frac{250 \text{ g}}{100 \text{ cm}^3}$$

$$D = 2.5 \text{ g/cm}^3$$

Your Turn!

1. A loaf of bread has a volume of 2270 cm³ and a mass of 454 g. What is the density of the bread?

____

2. A liter of water has a mass of 1000 g. What is the density of water? (Hint: 1 mL = 1 cm³)

____

3. A block of wood has a density of 0.6 g/cm³ and a volume of 1.2 cm³. What is the mass of the block of wood? Be careful!

____

4. Use the data below to calculate the density of each unknown substance. Then use the density chart above to determine the identity of each substance.

	Mass (g)	**Volume** (cm³)	**Density** (g/cm³)	**Substance**
	Example: 4725	350	4725 ÷ 350 = 13.5	mercury
a.	171	15	________	________
b.	108	40	________	________
c.	475	250	________	________
d.	680	1000	________	________

MATH IN SCIENCE: INTEGRATED SCIENCE

Name ______________________ Date __________ Class __________

WORKSHEET

MATH SKILLS USED
Multiplication
Division
Decimals
Percentages
Geometry

33 MATH IN SCIENCE: INTEGRATED SCIENCE

The Pressure Is On!

Use math to learn about force and pressure.

You are under pressure! Even though you may not be aware of it, the air above you presses down on every square centimeter of your body with the weight of a 1.03 kg mass! Because water is so much denser than air, pressure in water is many times greater than this. **Pressure** is defined as the force exerted on a particular area. The unit for pressure is the pascal (Pa), which is the force one newton (N) exerts on one square meter (m^2).

EQUATION:

$$\text{Pressure (Pa)} = \frac{\text{Force (N)}}{\text{Area (m}^2\text{)}}$$

Apply Some Pressure!

Use the equation for pressure to answer the following questions:

1. An elephant that weighs 40,000 N stands on one leg during a circus performance. The area on the bottom of the elephant's foot is 0.4 m^2. How much pressure is exerted on the elephant's foot?

____

2. A carpenter hammers a nail with a force of 45 N with every stroke. The head of the nail has a surface area of 0.002 m^2. How much pressure is exerted on the nailhead with each stroke?

____

3. A brick falls from the third floor of a construction site. The brick hits the ground on its end, which measures 0.15 m by 0.25 m, with a force of 30 N. How much pressure is exerted by the brick on the ground? (Hint: Area of a rectangle = width $\times$ length)

____

____

Pressure in the Atmosphere

The air pressure we live under is about 101,000 Pa at sea level. Use this value to complete the following problems. Show all your work.

4. A mountain climber climbs to the top of Mt. Everest, which at 8848 m is the highest point on Earth. Because most of the air in the atmosphere is below this altitude, air pressure is about 50% less at the peak than at sea level. What is the air pressure exerted on the mountain climber?

____

5. A meteorologist reports that air pressure is reduced 8,585 Pa by an approaching hurricane. What percentage change from normal air pressure does this represent?

____

____

Pressure in the Ocean

Water pressure increases approximately 10,000 Pa for every 1 m of depth. That means that the pressure at the bottom of a swimming pool that is 10 m deep is almost as great as the pressure exerted by the entire atmosphere!

6. Use what you know about water pressure to complete the chart.

Water Pressure at Various Depths

Depth (m)	1	2	7.5	100	500	1500
Water pressure (Pa)	10,000	20,000				

7. A sea turtle swims from a depth of 45 m to a depth of 28 m. What is the difference in water pressure between these two depths?

____

____

8. Deep Submergence Rescue Vehicles (DSRVs) can operate at depths of 4500 m.

a. If a DSRV with a surface area of 16 m^2 goes to this depth, what is the total force on the entire hull of the sub?

____

____

b. What would be the total force on a DSRV one-quarter that size at one-half that depth?

____

____

Challenge Yourself!

9. A magician lies on a bed of nails. The magician weighs 600 N and is supported by exactly 2000 nails. The tip of each nail has an area of 0.0001 m^2. Assuming that the weight of the magician is evenly distributed on the nails, how much pressure is exerted on each nail by the magician's body?

____

____

Name ______________________ Date ____________ Class ____________

WORKSHEET

34 **MATH IN SCIENCE: INTEGRATED SCIENCE**

MATH SKILLS USED
Multiplication
Division
Decimals

Sound Reasoning

Use your math skills to understand dolphin echolocation.

Dolphins use echolocation to find their way through murky waters. They do this by emitting a clicking sound and listening for an echo. The direction and delay of the echo give the dolphins information about what objects are nearby and where the objects are located.

1. Sound travels about 1530 m/s in sea water. How many times faster does sound travel in sea water than in air? (The speed of sound in air at 25°C is about 345 m/s.)

____

____

2. A dolphin emits a click that is reflected off an object. If it takes 0.2 seconds for the sound to be sent and to come back, how far away is the object?

____

____

3. How long would it take the sound to be sent and returned from the same object in air?

____

____

____

____

____

4. Assume that the speed of sound decreases by 6 m/s for every 10°C decrease in water temperature. If a dolphin swam to the Arctic Ocean, where the water is about 5°C, how would the dolphin's ability to estimate the distance to an object be affected?

____

____

____

____

____

____

____

Name ______________________ Date ____________ Class ____________

WORKSHEET
35 MATH IN SCIENCE: INTEGRATED SCIENCE

MATH SKILLS USED
Addition
Multiplication
Fractions
Decimals
Scientific Notation

Using Temperature Scales

Convert between degrees Fahrenheit and degrees Celsius.

Do you remember the last time you had your temperature taken? Your body temperature is usually about 98.6°F. This temperature is in degrees Fahrenheit (°F). The Fahrenheit temperature scale is a common temperature scale. In science class, however, a scale known as the Celsius (°C) scale is used. Temperatures in one scale can be mathematically converted to the other system using one of the equations below.

EQUATIONS: Conversion from Fahrenheit to Celsius: $\frac{5}{9} \times (°F - 32) = °C$

Conversion from Celsius to Fahrenheit: $\frac{9}{5} \times °C + 32 = °F$

SAMPLE PROBLEMS:

A. Convert 59°F to degrees Celcius.

$$°C = \frac{5}{9} \times (°F - 32)$$

$$°C = \frac{5}{9} \times (59 - 32)$$

$$°C = \frac{5}{9} \times 27$$

$$°C = \mathbf{15°C}$$

B. Convert 112°C to degrees Fahrenheit.

$$°F = \frac{9}{5} \times °C + 32$$

$$°F = \frac{9}{5} \times 112 + 32$$

$$°F = 201\frac{3}{5} + 32$$

$$°F = \mathbf{233\frac{3}{5}°F}$$

Turn Up the Temperature!

1. Convert the following temperatures from degrees Fahrenheit to degrees Celsius:

a. 98.6°F ____________________

b. 482°F ____________________

c. −4°F ____________________

2. Convert the following temperatures from degrees Celsius to degrees Fahrenheit:

a. 24°C ____________________

b. 17°C ____________________

c. 0°C ____________________

Challenge Yourself!

3. Convert 2.7×10^4°C to degrees Fahrenheit. ____________________

MATH IN SCIENCE: INTEGRATED SCIENCE

Name ______________________ Date ____________ Class ____________

WORKSHEET

36 MATH IN SCIENCE: INTEGRATED SCIENCE

Math Skills Used
Multiplication
Division
Fractions
Decimals
Percentages
Scientific Notation

Radioactive Decay and the Half-life

Use the half-lives of elements to learn about radioactive dating.

Most elements found in nature are stable; they do not change over time. Some elements, however, are unstable—that is, they change into a different element over time. Elements that go through this process of change are called **radioactive,** and the process of transformation is called **radioactive decay.** Because radioactive decay happens very steadily, scientists can use radioactive elements like clocks to measure the passage of time. By looking at how much of a certain element remains in an object and how much of it has decayed, scientists can determine an approximate age for the object.

So why are scientists interested in learning the ages of objects? By looking at very old things, such as rocks and fossils, and determining when they were formed, scientists learn about the history of the Earth and the plants and animals that have lived here. Radioactive dating makes this history lesson possible! A **half-life** is the time that it takes for half a certain amount of a radioactive material to decay, and it can range from less than a second to billions of years. The chart below lists the half-lives of some radioactive elements.

Table of Half-lives

Element	Half-life
Bismuth-212	60.5 minutes
Carbon-14	5730 years
Chlorine-36	400,000 years
Cobalt-60	5.26 years
Iodine-131	8.07 days

Element	Half-life
Phosphorous-24	14.3 days
Polonium-215	0.0018 seconds
Radium-226	1600 years
Sodium-24	15 hours
Uranium-238	4.5 billion years

1. Use the data in the table above to complete the following chart:

Table of Remaining Radium

Number of years after formation	0	1600	3200	6400	12,800
Percent of radium-226 remaining	100%	50%			

2. If 1 g of sodium-24 has decayed from a sample that was originally 2 g, how old is the sample?

____

____

3. What fraction of chlorine-36 remains undecayed after 200,000 years?

____

____

4. As uranium-238 decays, it becomes lead-206. After 3.5 g of uranium-238 decays for 1.125×10^9 years, how many grams of the sample will be lead-206?

5. A scientist has a 2.5 g sample of radium-226. How many grams of the sample will decay in 800 years?

6. An archaeologist finds a piece of old bone that she believes may be 2000 years old. The lab technician tells her that the carbon-14 in the bone has completed 25 percent of its first half-life. Does this finding support her belief about the age of the bone? Why or why not?

7. A technician does a test on an unidentified radioactive element and discovers that it has a half-life of 4.5×10^9 years. What element do you think it is, and why?

8. A paleontologist unearths the remains of a *Tyrannosaurus rex*. We know that these dinosaurs became extinct about 65 million years ago. Therefore, would it be reasonable to expect that the carbon-14 in the fossil has completed 15,000 half-lives? Why or why not?

Name ______________________ Date ____________ Class ____________

WORKSHEET

37 **MATH IN SCIENCE: INTEGRATED SCIENCE**

MATH SKILLS USED
Multiplication
Decimals
Percentages
Scientific Notation
The Unit Factor and Dimensional Analysis

Rain-Forest Math

Calculate the damage to the world's rain forests.

Tropical rain forests now cover about 7 percent of the Earth's land surface; however, about half the original forests have been cut during the last 50 years. An additional 2 percent of the total remaining tropical rain forest is being cut each year.

The Damage Done

1. Approximately what percentage of the Earth's surface was covered by rain forest 50 years ago?

2. The land surface of the Earth is approximately 1.49×10^8 km^2. How many square kilometers of that is rain forest today? Give your answer in scientific notation.

3. Suppose a certain rain forest consists of 500,000 km^2. The amount of rainfall per square meter per day is 20 L. If 2 percent of this rain forest is cut this year, how much water will be lost to next year's water cycle? Show all your work.

Name ______________________ Date ____________ Class ____________

WORKSHEET **38** **MATH IN SCIENCE: LIFE SCIENCE**

MATH SKILLS USED
Addition
Subtraction

Knowing Nutrition

Use a Calorie chart and an activity chart to learn about how we consume and burn the energy in food.

The food we eat provides the energy we need to work, play, and stay healthy. The energy in food is measured in **calories (cal)**, which is the thermal energy required to raise the temperature of 1 g of water 1°C. Because a single calorie is such a small amount of energy, nutritionists and food makers use the **kilocalorie (C)**, or 1,000 calories, to measure the energy in food and drinks. The number of Calories a person needs to consume each day depends largely on his or her body size and level of activity. The more active a person is, the more Calories he or she needs to keep going. The chart below shows Calorie counts for single servings of some common foods.

Calorie Count

Food	C
Apple	81
American cheese	105
Baked potato with sour cream	393
Baked chicken, white meat	142
Wheat bread	70
Carrots	31
Cola	152
Corn flakes	100
French fries	235
Plain hamburger	275

Food	C
Low-fat milk	90
Orange juice	112
Pancake	61
Pancake syrup	50
Peanut butter	188
Cheese pizza	140
Scrambled egg	100
Spaghetti	260
Vanilla ice cream	184
Vegetable soup	78

Counting Your Calories

1. Use the data in the Calorie chart to calculate the total number of Calories consumed in each of the following meals. Be sure to show your work.

a. Breakfast
2 scrambled eggs
1 slice of bread
1 glass of orange juice
1 pancake

Calorie total = ____________

b. Lunch
1 peanut-butter sandwich
(2 slices of bread)
1 bowl of soup
1 apple
1 cola

Calorie total = ____________

c. **Dinner**
1 baked potato ____________
2 pieces of chicken
1 glass of milk ____________
2 servings of carrots
1 ice cream ____________

____

____

Calorie total = ____________

2. How many Calories were consumed in the entire day?

____

Activity Chart

The following chart shows the approximate number of Calories burned in half an hour of exercise. Note that Calories burned varies with a person's mass and type of excercise.

Calories Burned Per Half Hour of Excercise

	Body mass (kg)				
Activity	**32–42**	**43–49**	**50–57**	**58–66**	**67–75**
Basketball	123	155	195	240	280
Bicycling	185	225	260	300	340
Bowling	30	35	39	45	52
Jogging	243	287	330	385	440
Skating	96	108	120	135	149
Soccer	156	186	220	266	312
Swimming	182	215	248	292	336
Volleyball	150	173	195	225	255
Walking	108	126	144	168	192

Hint: To convert weight in pounds (lb) to mass in kilograms (kg), multiply pounds by 0.45.

Use the data from the activity chart above to answer the following questions:

3. How many Calories does a 55 kg person burn in half an hour of swimming, half an hour of playing basketball, and an hour of walking?

____

4. How many fewer Calories are burned in half an hour of bowling by a 74 kg person than in half an hour of jogging by a 40 kg person?

____

____

5. A 44 kg girl eats a lunch of a hamburger with cheese, a serving of French fries, and a cola. Would an hour of jogging burn off the Calories she consumed?

6. The "special of the day" at the cafeteria is one piece of baked chicken, a bowl of soup, carrots, and a glass of milk. You know that you will be skating after school for one hour. Assuming that you have a mass of 66 kg, will this meal give you enough energy for your workout?

7. How long would a 64 kg person have to play volleyball to burn 450 C?

8. How many more Calories does a 41 kg person burn in half an hour of jogging than a 60 kg person who spends the same amount of time walking?

9. After an hour of playing basketball, two 75 kg members of the team go out to lunch. They each consume two hamburgers and a cola. How many more Calories did they consume than burn?

Long-term Challenge

10. Design a three-day menu for yourself, and calculate the total number of Calories you would consume. Then design an exercise program that burns approximately the same number of Calories as you consume. Use a variety of different foods and physical activities in your plans.

Name ______________________ Date ____________ Class ____________

WORKSHEET

39 **MATH IN SCIENCE: LIFE SCIENCE**

MATH SKILLS USED
Addition
Subtraction
Multiplication
Division
Averages
Fractions
Percentages
Geometry

Random Samples: Estimating Population

Use your math skills to learn about the use and accuracy of random population samples.

"Why did we bother with a picnic anyway? These ants are everywhere," Gina complained. "There must be a million ants on our blanket!" Dylan agreed. Of course, Gina and Dylan were exaggerating. But suppose they really did want to know how many ants were in the park. How could they find out? Counting each ant would be very difficult; ants are tiny, and they live in a large area, have a large population, and move around a lot. To solve this problem, Gina and Dylan could use a mathematical tool called a **random sample** to estimate the total population of ants in the park. To take a random sample, they would count the ants in a particular region of the park. To estimate the total population of ants in the park, they would first divide the total area of the park by the area of the sample region. Then they would multiply that number by the number of ants they counted in the random sample.

The following diagram shows the section of the park where Gina and Dylan had their picnic. Each dot represents 25 ants. Use the diagram to answer the questions.

	A	B	C	D	E
1	• •	• • •	•	• • • •	•
2	• • •		• • • •	• • •	• • • •
3	• • • •	• • • •	• • • • •	• •	
4		• • •	• •	•	• • •
5	• •		• • • •		• • • • •

1. Each square on the grid represents 1 m^2 of the picnic area. What is the size of the picnic area?

____

Taking a Random Sample

In order to get a closer population estimate, count the number of ants in a selection of squares that are chosen at random. Then answer the following questions. Each square can be identified by a letter and a number. For example, the first square at the top left is square A1.

Name ______________________ Date ____________ Class ____________

2. The following is a randomly chosen selection of squares. Calculate the number of ants found in each of these squares. (1 dot = 25 ants)

   a. D2 ______________ b. E4 ______________

   c. E2 ______________ d. B1 ______________

   e. D3 ______________ f. C5 ______________

   g. C3 ______________ h. A4 ______________

3. What is the average number of ants per square meter in the sampled area?

   ____

4. Using the average from item 3, estimate the ants' total population.

   ____

How Accurate Was the Estimated Population?

You can check the accuracy of the estimated population by finding the **percent error.** The closer your percent error is to zero, the more accurate your estimate is. In order to calculate the percent error, you must know the exact population, so count all of the dots to find the exact population of the ants before continuing.

5. Use the following equation to find the percent error of your estimate. (Hint: If the value you determine by subtracting the exact population from the estimated population is negative, use the absolute value in your calculations.)

$$\text{percent error} = \frac{\text{estimated population} - \text{exact population}}{\text{exact population}} \times 100$$

   ____

   ____

6. Make a random selection of five squares from the grid, and determine the estimated population based on your random sample. Then calculate the percent error as you did in question 5. How does your percent error compare with the percent error found in question 5?

   ____

   ____

   ____

Name ______________________ Date ____________ Class ____________

WORKSHEET

40 **MATH IN SCIENCE: LIFE SCIENCE**

MATH SKILLS USED
Multiplication
Decimals
Percentages

Punnett Square Popcorn

Use the Punnett Square to learn about dominance and codominance in inherited traits.

You are a cofounder of Flav-R-Gro, Inc., a company that specializes in creating genetically engineered foods. You and your partner, Maisie Mantequilla, have recently been concentrating on developing new types of corn. Together, you have developed a type of corn that, fresh from the stalk, tastes like it has been roasted with just the perfect amount of butter and salt! Your new creation, which you and Maisie call WonderCorn, is bringing you the admiration of your peers and the loyalty of customers. Hungry corn consumers are eager to try your tasty creation because they can eat it without worrying about the health risks caused by adding butter and salt to food. You and Maisie succeeded through determination, hard work, and an understanding of *codominance.*

Background

In some cases of genetic inheritance, two dominant traits are expressed together instead of one trait being dominant and one trait being recessive. This phenomenon is known as **codominance.** When codominance occurs, both traits are evident in the phenotype. For example, a cross between a homozygous red horse and a homozygous white horse results in offspring with a roan coat, which consists of both red hairs and white hairs. Human blood types are also determined by codominant traits.

You and Maisie suspected that the taste trait in corn was codominant. To find out, you crossed two other types of corn that you created: a homozygous salty corn (*SS*) and a homozygous buttery corn (*BB*). The offspring were all WonderCorn. See the Punnett square below for this cross.

	B	*B*
S	*SB*	*SB*
S	*SB*	*SB*

Solve the Punnet Problems!

1. What is the genotype of WonderCorn?

____

2. What percentage of the offspring have this genotype?

____

Your hunch about the codominant taste traits was right. You and Maisie then did another Punnett square to predict the offspring that would be produced by a second-generation (heterozygous) cross. Complete the cross in the Punnett square below.

	S	*B*
S		
B		

3. What percentage of these offspring will be WonderCorn?

____

4. What percentage of these offspring could you and Maisie use for another homozygous cross?

____

5. If the heterozygous cross produces 736 offspring, how many will be WonderCorn? Show your work.

____

6. How many of the 736 offspring will taste salty but not buttery? Show your work.

____

7. The demand for WonderCorn has been high! Grover's Grocery alone has ordered 50 bushels for delivery as soon as possible. Flav-R-Gro, Inc., is fresh out of WonderCorn, but you and Maisie are beginning another growing cycle. Would you be better off using a homozygous cross or a heterozygous cross to fill the order for Grover's Grocery? Explain your answer.

____

____

____

____

____

Name ______________________ Date ____________ Class ____________

WORKSHEET

41 MATH IN SCIENCE: LIFE SCIENCE

MATH SKILLS USED
Multiplication
Division
Decimals
SI Measurement and Conversion

Scale of Organisms

Use the SI system to compare the sizes of some of the smallest and largest organisms on Earth.

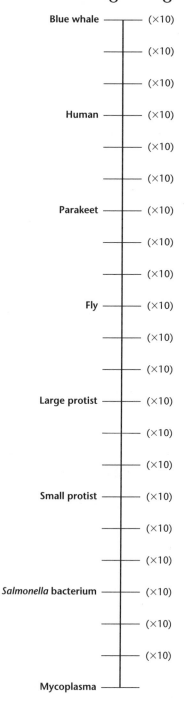

Blue whale	(×10)
	(×10)
	(×10)
Human	(×10)
	(×10)
	(×10)
Parakeet	(×10)
	(×10)
	(×10)
Fly	(×10)
	(×10)
	(×10)
Large protist	(×10)
	(×10)
	(×10)
Small protist	(×10)
	(×10)
	(×10)
Salmonella bacterium	(×10)
	(×10)
	(×10)
Mycoplasma	

Mass is the amount of matter that composes an object or living thing. Look at the scale showing the range of masses of living things. Each division of the scale represents a factor of 10, in terms of the mass of the organism. For example, the blue whale, which is the largest animal alive today, is three divisions above a human. Its mass is therefore $10 \times 10 \times 10$ (or 1000 times) the mass of a human. In the same way, a human has a mass 1000 times that of a parakeet.

Use the scale to complete the following exercises:

1. The parakeet has a mass 1000 times that of what other living thing?

   ____

2. A large protist has a mass ______________ times that of a small protist.

3. A *Salmonella* bacterium has a mass 1000 times that of a ______________.

4. A small protist has a mass ______________ times that of a mycoplasma.

5. A human has a mass ______________ times greater than a large protist.

6. A fly's mass is 1,000,000,000 times greater than a ______________.

7. A blue whale is 25 m long, while a mycoplasma is 0.3 μm long. How many mycoplasmas placed end to end would stretch from one end of the whale to the other?

   ____

Name ______________________ Date ____________ Class ____________

WORKSHEET

42 MATH IN SCIENCE: EARTH SCIENCE

MATH SKILLS USED
Multiplication
Division
Decimals
Percentages
SI Measurement and Conversion
Geometry

Sedimentation in the Grand Canyon

Use your math skills to study the Colorado River's rate of sedimentation in the Grand Canyon.

Imagine that you are a geologist and that you read the following excerpt in a geological journal:

> **EARTH ALERT:** A gradual change in the global climate is causing the Colorado River to slowly deposit sediment in the Grand Canyon. Scientists estimate that the present rate of deposition is raising the canyon floor by 0.05 mm per year.

Your geological interests lead you to ask some questions. Suppose that you've organized your questions and concerns into the following itemized list. Using your mathematical knowledge, answer the following six items about the fate of the Grand Canyon.

Question List

ITEM 1: If the canyon is 1500 m deep, how long will it be until the river completely fills the canyon with sediment? Show your work.

____

____

____

____

ITEM 2: Make a graph on the grid below to show the amount of sediment deposited in the Grand Canyon over an average human lifetime (about 75 years in the United States). Make sure to label the *x*-axis and *y*-axis and to give your graph a title.

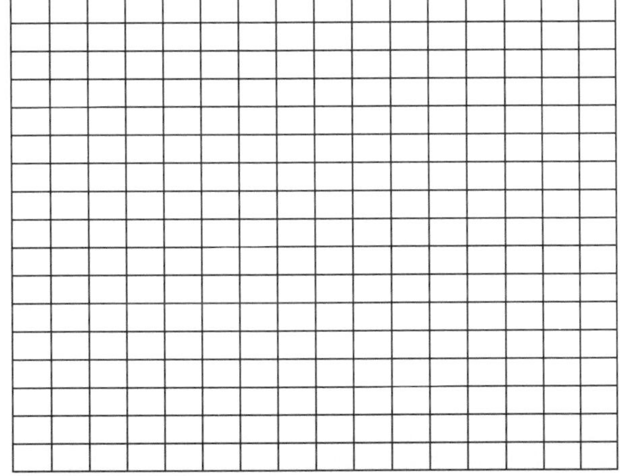

ITEM 3: Some geologists believe that the sedimentation rate of the Colorado River could increase in the future. If the rate of deposition increases by 40%, how much does the river deposit per year?

____

____

____

ITEM 4: What will be the total volume of sediment dumped into the canyon if the canyon is 2 km wide and 30 km long? Show your work.

____

____

____

____

____

ITEM 5: If the same amount of sediment from Item 4 were instead carried to the mouth of the river and dumped into the ocean, a delta would form. Assuming that the ocean is 500 m deep at the mouth of the river and that the elevation of the new land at the delta is at sea level, what will be the surface area of the delta? Show your work. (Hint: area = volume ÷ depth)

____

____

Critical Thinking Challenge

ITEM 6: An animal is buried by the sediment at the bottom of the canyon. If a fossil hunter finds the animal 1 million years after the canyon is completely filled, how old will the fossil be? Explain your answer.

____

____

____

____

____

____

____

Name ______________________ Date ____________ Class ____________

WORKSHEET 43 **MATH IN SCIENCE: EARTH SCIENCE**

MATH SKILLS USED
Addition
Percentages
Powers of 10

Earthquake Power!

Use the Richter scale to compare the size and magnitude of earthquakes.

Sometimes earthquakes are strong enough to cause a huge amount of damage—highways crumble and buildings fall in an instant. Other times, earthquakes can be so slight that people hardly feel them. Scientists use a mathematical system called the Richter scale to compare the size and magnitude of earthquakes. An earthquake's magnitude depends on the amplitude of seismic waves, which are recorded by a seismograph. The greater the amplitude of the waves is, the higher the reading on the Richter scale is.

Part 1: Richter Readings

Earthquakes per year	Magnitude on the Richter scale*	Severity
1	8.0 and higher	great
18	7.0–7.9	major
120	6.0–6.9	strong
800	5.0–5.9	moderate
6200	4.0–4.9	light
49,000	3.0–3.9	minor

*Earthquakes measuring less than 3.0 are not included because approximately 9000 occur daily.

Use What You Know!

Use the table above to answer the following questions. Remember to show your work.

1. In a given year, how many earthquakes measure 6.0 or greater?

____

____

2. In a given year, what percentage of earthquakes measure 3.0 or greater are moderate?

____

____

3. Calculate the percentage of earthquakes that measure 5.0 or greater that are classified as "major" and "great."

____

____

MATH IN SCIENCE: EARTH SCIENCE

Part 2: Richter Math

The Richter scale is based on a mathematical system. Each whole-number increase in magnitude on the Richter scale represents an increase in measured amplitude by a factor of 10. That means that an earthquake measuring 4.0 on the Richter scale is 10 times as strong as an earthquake measuring 3.0.

The Richter scale is also used to estimate the relative energy released by earthquakes. Each whole-number increase on the Richter scale represents an increase in energy release by a factor of 32. Examine the table below, and work the problems that follow. Be sure to show your work.

The Richter Scale

Difference in magnitude	Relative strength	Change of energy released
0.3	2.0 times as strong	3 times as much
0.5	3.2 times as strong	5.5 times as much
1	10 (10^1) times as strong	32 times as much
2	100 (10^2) times as strong	32^2 times as much
3	1000 (10^3) times as strong	32^3 times as much
4	10,000 (10^4) times as strong	32^4 times as much
5	100,000 (10^5) times as strong	32^5 times as much

4. On December 16, 1920, an earthquake measuring 8.6 on the Richter scale hit Gansu, a province in China. Twelve years later, an earthquake measuring 7.6 hit Gansu. How much stronger was the 1920 earthquake?

____

5. How much more energy did the 1920 earthquake release compared with the second earthquake?

____

6. In 1906, an earthquake occurred in San Francisco that measured 8.3 on the Richter scale. In 1994, an earthquake occurred in Northridge, California, that measured 6.7 on the Richter scale.

a. How much stronger was the San Francisco earthquake?

____

____

b. How much more energy did the San Francisco earthquake release?

____

____

Name ______________________ Date __________ Class __________

WORKSHEET

44 MATH IN SCIENCE: EARTH SCIENCE

MATH SKILLS USED
Multiplication
Division
Decimals
Scientific Notation
SI Measurement and Conversion

Distances in Space

Learn about the units of length used to measure distances in our solar system and beyond.

Because astronomers study objects over such extremely large distances, astronomers commonly use units of length that are much bigger than the ones we usually use. Two common units of distance used in astronomy are the astronomical unit (AU) and the light-year.

Astronomical Unit

The astronomical unit (AU) is the average distance from the Earth to the sun, measured to be about 1.5×10^8 km. It is a convenient unit to use when discussing distances within our solar system.

1. Saturn has an average distance of 9.5 AU from the sun. How many centimeters is this?

____

____

2. Pluto, the outermost planet in the solar system, is about 6×10^9 km from the sun. How many astronomical units (AU) is this?

____

____

Light-year

The light-year is defined as the distance that light travels in a year. (The speed of light is 3×10^5 km/s.) For instance, Alpha Centauri, the closest star to the Earth after the sun, is 4.3 light-years from us.

3. How long does it take light from this star to reach us?

____

4. The star Betelgeuse, meaning "armpit of the giant," is 310 light-years from Earth. How many hours does light from this star take to reach Earth?

____

____

5. How many AUs are in a light-year? (*Hint:* There are approximately 31,536,000 seconds in a year.)

____

____

Name ______________________________ Date ______________ Class ______________

WORKSHEET

45 **MATH IN SCIENCE: EARTH SCIENCE**

MATH SKILLS USED
Subtraction
Division
Decimals
Percentages
Scientific Notation

Geologic Time Scale

Understand geologic time using the geologic time scale.

If you wanted to find out how long it has been since your last birthday, you would simply look at a yearly calendar, right? But what would you do if you wanted to find out how long ago a dinosaur lived or a volcano was formed? Then you would need a calendar that goes much farther back in time—maybe all the way back to the beginning of Earth's history. There is such a calendar—it is called the **geologic time scale.** It begins about 4.6 billion years ago and continues up to the present. Instead of months and days, it divides Earth's history into *eons, eras,* and *periods.*

Geologic Time Scale

Eon	Era	Period	Millions of years ago
Phanerozoic	Cenozoic	Quaternary	1.8
		Tertiary	65
	Mesozoic	Cretaceous	144
		Jurassic	206
		Triassic	248
	Paleozoic	Permian	290
		Pennsylvanian	323
		Mississippian	354
		Devonian	417
		Silurian	443
		Ordovician	490
		Cambrian	540
Proterozoic			2500
Archean			3800
Hadean			4600

It's Been a Long, Long Time . . .

1. Calculate the number of years that each era and eon lasted, starting with the present era.

____

____

____

____

2. How many years passed between the end of the Pennsylvanian period and the beginning of the Tertiary period? Be careful!

____

Managing Huge Numbers

The geologic time scale measures extremely long periods of time. When numbers are very large, it is often easier to do calculations or comparisons using scientific notation, which simplifies large numbers.

3. Write the following times in scientific notation:

a. the beginning of the Quaternary period ______________

b. the end of the Proterozoic eon ______________

c. the beginning of the Earth's history ______________

d. the beginning of the Jurassic period ______________

e. the end of the Jurassic period ______________

4. The Archean eon lasted 1.3×10^9 years. The era in which we live, the Cenozoic, meaning "recent life," has lasted 6.5×10^7 years. How many times longer was the Archean eon than the present era?

____

____

The Fossil Record

As plants and animals appeared and disappeared from the Earth, they left a fossil record. In fact, the divisions in the geologic time scale are based on distinct changes in the fossil record. For example, the extinction of the dinosaurs separates the Mesozoic era from the Cenozoic era. In the chart below, you can see that the appearance of different living things characterizes different periods in the Earth's history.

Animals in the Fossil Record

Animals	First appearance
Birds	Jurassic period (late)
Mammals	Jurassic period (early)
Reptiles	Pennsylvanian period
Amphibians	Mississippian period
Fishes	Ordovician period

5. Approximately how much longer have fishes been on Earth than mammals?

____

____

6. The earliest plant life began to appear on land during the Silurian period, about 420 million years ago. During approximately what percentage of the total history of the Earth were plants *not* growing on land?

____

____

Calendar Challenge

Another way to understand the geologic time scale is to picture Earth's history as it would appear on a typical calendar. To begin, determine how many years a "day" is in geologic time. Then determine in which months the eras fall. Fill in the calendar below with the names of the eras. Write the name of the eon if there is no name for the era.

Earth's Historical Calendar

January (31 days)	February (28 days)	March (31 days)	April (30 days)
May (31 days)	**June (30 days)**	**July (31 days)**	**August (31 days)**
September (30 days)	**October (31 days)**	**November (30 days)**	**December (31 days)**

7. How many years in geologic time is represented by one day on the calendar above?

____

8. On what date does the Proterozoic eon end?

____

9. How many days did the Paleozoic era last?

____

10. How many days are there from the beginning of the Cenozoic era to the end of the year?

____

Name ______________________________ Date ____________ Class ____________

WORKSHEET

46 **MATH IN SCIENCE: EARTH SCIENCE**

Mapping and Surveying

MATH SKILLS USED
Addition
Multiplication
Division
Decimals
Geometry

Use geometry to analyze maps and solid figures.

When scientists survey an area, they often represent the length, width, and other measurements on a map or diagram. This data can then be used in mathematical equations to determine the area of a piece of land, the volume of a lake, or the dimensions of a mountainside.

Part 1: Perimeter and Area

	Rectangle	Triangle	Odd shapes
	a, b	a, b, d, c	
Perimeter	$(2 \times a) + (2 \times b)$	$a + b + c$	Divide or approximate to a combination of rectangles and triangles, and add their perimeters or areas.
Area	$a \times b$	$\frac{c \times d}{2}$	

The map below shows a survey of a park. Each square of the grid represents one square meter, or 1 m^2. Use the equations above to answer the questions below.

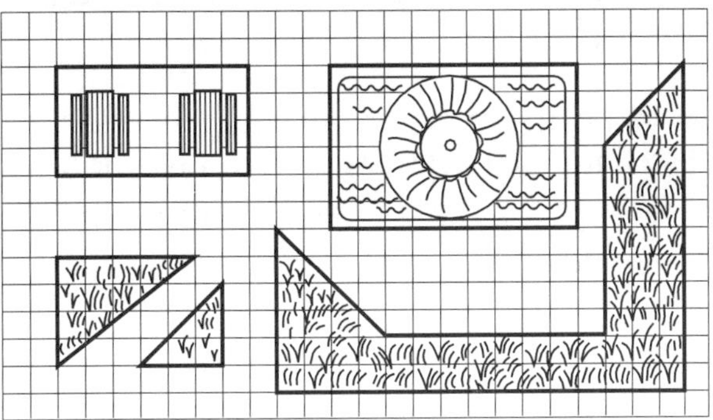

Map It Out!

1. How long is the perimeter of the picnic area?

____

2. What is the total area of the picnic area?

____

3. How much area in the park has grass?

____

4. Estimate the area covered by the fountain, not including the rectangular pool.

____

Part 2: Calculating Volume

To find the volume of a cube or prism, multiply the height times the width times the length, as follows:

$$\text{Volume} = 5\text{ m} \times 8\text{ m} \times 15\text{ m}$$
$$\text{Volume} = \mathbf{600\ m^3}$$

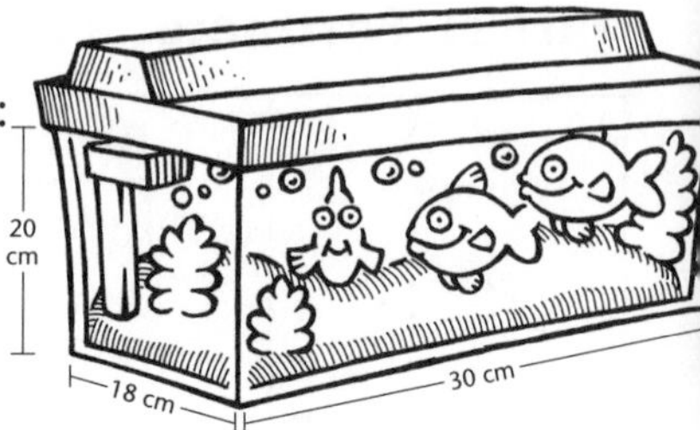

Use the equation for volume to answer the following questions:

5. Each fish in the aquarium shown at right needs 3500 cm^3 of water to live comfortably. Do the fish in this tank have enough space?

____

____

6. The Burnside family vegetable garden measures 4 m × 3.5 m. A garden planning guide suggests mixing fertilizer with the soil to a depth of 25 cm. In cubic meters, what will be the total volume of fertilizer-soil mix in the garden?

____

A Lock System

A lock is an enclosed part of a canal or waterway equipped with gates that allow the water level in each lock to be changed. Locks are used to raise or lower boats from one level to another.

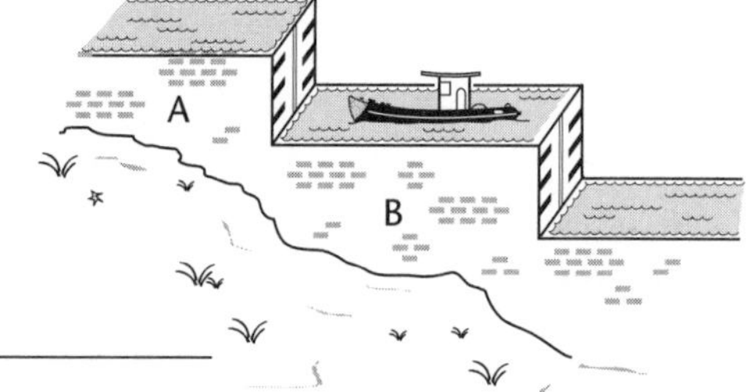

7. Lock A is 8 m deep, 16 m wide, and 22 m long. What is the capacity of the lock?

____

____

____

Challenge Yourself!

8. Lock B, which is the same width as Lock A, is 1.5 times as long and has a volume of 4488 m^3. How deep is Lock B?

____

____

Name ______________________ Date ____________ Class ____________

WORKSHEET

47 MATH IN SCIENCE: PHYSICAL SCIENCE

MATH SKILLS USED
Addition
Subtraction
Multiplication
Division
Averages
Decimals
Percentages

Average Speed in a Pinewood Derby

Determine the average speeds of a Pinewood Derby car.

Cindy and Santiago have just finished building model cars for their school's annual Pinewood Derby. In order to test their cars, Santiago sets Cindy's car at the top of a 240 cm long ramp and releases it. Cindy uses a stopwatch to measure how long it takes the car to reach the bottom of the ramp. The two decide to conduct three trials for each car and then calculate the overall average speeds. Cindy recorded her initial results in the table below.

Cindy's Car

Trial	Time (s)	Average speed (cm/s)
1	8	
2	10	
3	8	

The Race Is On!

1. Complete the third column of the chart, and show your work below.

____

____

2. What was the overall average speed of Cindy's car?

____

____

3. Santiago's car has an overall average speed of 25 cm/s. If he could increase his car's overall average speed by 10%, what would his car's new overall average speed be?

____

____

4. By adding lubricant to the wheels of his car, Santiago determines that he can increase his car's average speed to 29.5 cm/s. What percentage increase does this represent?

____

____

Name ______________________________ Date ____________ Class ____________

WORKSHEET

48 MATH IN SCIENCE: PHYSICAL SCIENCE

Newton: Force and Motion

MATH SKILLS USED
Subtraction
Multiplication
Decimals
Scientific Notation

Use the equations for acceleration and Newton's second law to learn about the motions and forces in the world around us.

In the seventeenth century, a brilliant young scientist named Isaac Newton explained the relationship between force, mass, and acceleration. This simple relationship describes much of the force and motion in the universe, from a tossed baseball to the motion of the stars and planets.

Part 1: Acceleration

Have you ever seen the start of an auto race? In one instant, the cars are practically motionless. The next instant, they are almost flying around the track. What acceleration! But did you know that as a speeding car slows to turn, it is also accelerating? **Acceleration** is defined as the rate at which the velocity of an object changes. In other words, acceleration is a measure of how quickly something speeds up *or* slows down. The equation for acceleration is given below.

EQUATION: change in velocity = final velocity − initial velocity

$$\text{acceleration} = \frac{\text{change in velocity}}{\text{time}}$$

SAMPLE PROBLEM: What is the acceleration of an in-line skater who increases her velocity from 3.5 m/s forward to 6 m/s forward in 2 seconds?

$$\text{change in velocity} = 6 \text{ m/s} - 3.5 \text{ m/s} = 2.5 \text{ m/s}$$

$$\text{acceleration} = \frac{2.5 \text{ m/s}}{2 \text{ s}}$$

acceleration = **1.25 m/s² forward**

1. Calculate the acceleration of the ball for each time period that it falls.

a. ______________________________

b. ______________________________

c. ______________________________

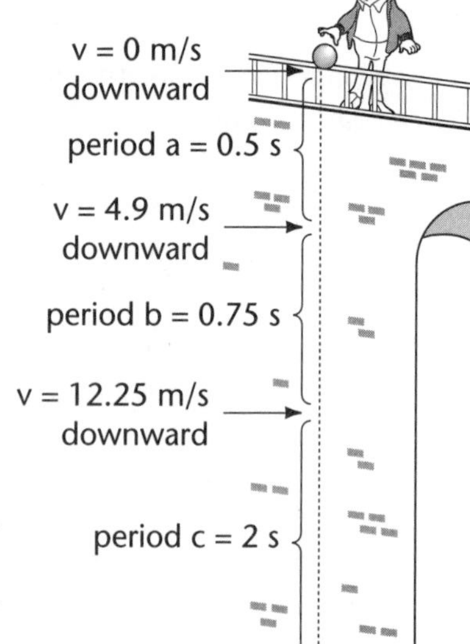

Challenge Yourself!

2. A jet flying at 200 m/s north accelerates at a rate of 18.2 m/s² for 15 seconds. What is the jet's final velocity?

____

____

____

Part 2: Newton's Second Law

Isaac Newton expressed the relationship between force, mass, and acceleration in his second law. This law is so important that it became the basis for much of modern physics. In fact, Newton's contribution to science was so great that the unit for force, the newton (N), was named after him. A newton is defined as the force needed to produce an acceleration of 1 m/s^2 on a 1 kg object. Therefore, $1 \text{ N} = 1 \text{ kg} \times 1 \text{ m/s}^2$. The equation for Newton's second law is given below.

EQUATION:

$$\text{Force} = \text{mass} \times \text{acceleration}$$
$$F = m \times a$$

If you know two of the values in this equation, you can calculate the third by changing the equation around, as follows:

$$\text{acceleration} = \frac{\text{Force}}{\text{mass}} \quad \textit{and} \quad \text{mass} = \frac{\text{Force}}{\text{acceleration}}$$

SAMPLE PROBLEM: A soccer ball accelerates at a rate of 22 m/s^2 forward when kicked by a player. The soccer ball has a mass of 0.5 kg. How much force was applied to the ball to produce this acceleration?

$$\text{Force} = \text{mass} \times \text{acceleration}$$
$$\text{Force} = 0.5 \text{ kg} \times 22 \text{ m/s}^2$$
$$\text{Force} = 11 \text{ kg} \times \text{m/s}^2$$
$$\text{Force} = \mathbf{11\ N}$$

Use the equations above to complete the following problems:

3. Calculate the force necessary to accelerate the following vehicles at the rate of acceleration shown in the illustration.

a.

Force = ________________________

b.

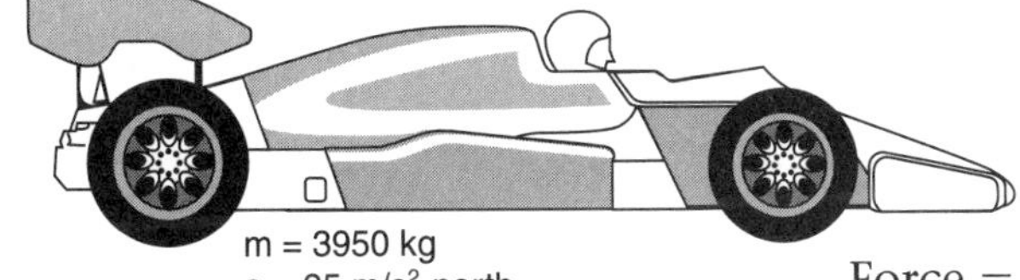

Force = ________________________

c.

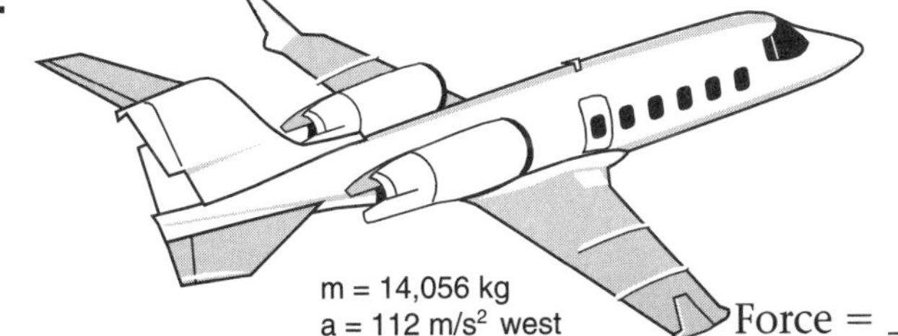

Force = ________________________

4. How much force is needed to move a 0.1 kg snowball at a rate of 15 m/s^2 upward?

---

5. A 0.02 N push accelerates a table-tennis ball along a table at 8 m/s^2 north. What is the mass of the ball?

---

6. At lift-off, an astronaut on the space shuttle experiences an acceleration of approximately 35 m/s^2 upward. What force does an 80 kg astronaut experience during this acceleration?

---

7. What is the acceleration of a train with a mass of 3.2×10^9 kg that pushes itself forward with 2.4×10^{10} N of force?

Part 3: The Force of Gravity

Forces are not always exerted on objects by direct physical contact, such as a hand pushing a door closed. For instance, the Earth exerts the force of gravity on objects even when the objects are not directly touching the ground. The acceleration on an object due to the force of gravity is 9.8 m/s^2 downward. In other words, for every second an object is falling, its velocity increases by 9.8 m/s downward.

8. a. A 9 kg bowling ball rolls off a table and strikes the ground. If the ball is in the air for 0.5 seconds, how fast is the ball moving when it hits the ground?

---

b. Another bowling ball with one-fifth less mass rolls off the same table and strikes the ground. When this ball hits the ground, is it moving faster, slower, or the same speed as the first ball? Explain your answer.

Name ______________________ Date __________ Class __________

WORKSHEET

49 MATH IN SCIENCE: PHYSICAL SCIENCE

MATH SKILLS USED
Multiplication Decimals

Momentum

Use the equation for momentum to describe an object's motion.

Imagine yourself speeding down a hill on your bicycle without using your brakes. As you reach the bottom of the hill, do you stop? No, you keep on going, until a force, such as the friction between your tires and the road or your brakes, brings you to a stop. The faster you are going or the more mass you have, the more force will be necessary to bring you to a stop. This property is **momentum** (p), which is the product of the mass of an object and its velocity. In an equation, it looks like this:

EQUATION: momentum = mass × velocity

$$p = m \times v$$

SAMPLE PROBLEM: A gymnast with a mass of 62 kg runs at a velocity of 11 m/s toward a pommel horse. What is her momentum?

momentum = mass × velocity

$$p = 62 \text{ kg} \times 11 \text{ m/s}$$

p = **682 kg × m/s toward the pommel horse**

Momentous Momentum

Use the equation for momentum to answer the following questions. Show your work.

1. Find the momentum of the different balls.

m = 0.045 kg
v = 16 m/s upward

m = 0.168 kg
v = 3 m/s forward

m = 0.575 kg
v = 9.2 m/s east

p = ______________ p = ______________ p = ______________

2. At a rodeo, a bucking bronco throws an 81 kg rider into the air at a velocity of 10 m/s upward. What is the rider's momentum?

____

3. Two passengers are riding in a boat that has a mass of 1500 kg. The two passengers together have a mass of 180 kg. What is the momentum of the boat and passengers when the boat is traveling at a velocity of 15 m/s west?

____

Challenge Yourself!

4. What is the velocity of a 55 kg skater who has a momentum of 440 kg × m/s forward?

____

Name ______________________ Date __________ Class __________

WORKSHEET

50 MATH IN SCIENCE: PHYSICAL SCIENCE

MATH SKILLS USED
Addition
Multiplication

Balancing Chemical Equations

Learn to balance chemical equations.

A **chemical equation** is an easy way to represent a chemical reaction—it shows you which elements react together and what the resulting products will be. In the equation, the reactants are on the left side of the arrow, and the products are on the right side of the arrow. A balanced chemical equation has an equal number of atoms of each element in the reactants and the products.

PROCEDURE: To balance a chemical reaction, count the number of atoms of each element in both the reactants and the products. Then determine the numbers that, when multiplied by the number of atoms in the reactants or products, will make the number of atoms on either side of the arrow equal. These numbers are known as *coefficients*. Next check the equation by counting the number of atoms in the reactants and the products. If the equation is balanced, the number of atoms on each side will be the same.

SAMPLE PROBLEM: $Zn + HBr \rightarrow H_2 + ZnBr_2$

Step 1: Count the number of atoms of each element in the reactants and in the products.

Step 1

Reactants	Products
1 Zn	1 Zn
1 H	2 H
1 Br	2 Br

Step 2: Determine the number that, when multiplied by the one or more atoms in the reactants or products, will make the number of atoms on either side of the arrow equal. Because we have two H atoms and two Br atoms in the product, we can multiply the reactant HBr by a coefficient of 2, as follows:

$$Zn + 2HBr \rightarrow H_2 + ZnBr_2$$

Step 3: Check the equation by counting the number of atoms of each element on each side of the equation. Because there are the same number of atoms of each element in the reactants and the products, you know the equation is balanced.

Step 3

Reactants	Products
1 Zn	1 Zn
2 H	2 H
2 Br	2 Br

A Balancing Act

Balance the following chemical equations:

1. $Na + Cl_2 \rightarrow NaCl$ ______________________

2. $Ca + Cl_2 \rightarrow CaCl_2$ ______________________

3. $H_2O \rightarrow H_2 + O_2$ ______________________

4. $Cu + AgCl \rightarrow Ag + CuCl_2$ ______________________

5. $FeCl_2 + K_2S \rightarrow FeS + KCl$ ______________________

Name ______________________ Date ____________ Class ____________

WORKSHEET

51 MATH IN SCIENCE: PHYSICAL SCIENCE

Work and Power

MATH SKILLS USED
Addition
Multiplication
Division
Decimals
Scientific Notation

Use the equations for work and power.

Part 1: An Equation for Work

As you sit and read this worksheet, are you doing work? You might say, "Yes, of course." But are you doing work in the scientific sense? Scientists use the word *work* to describe a very specific concept. In physics, **work** is a force applied over a distance.

EQUATION:

$$\text{work} = \text{Force} \times \text{distance}$$
$$W = F \times d$$

The SI unit for work is the newton-meter (N · m), also known as a **joule (J).** You can calculate the amount of work accomplished with the equation above. Let's see how it's done!

SAMPLE PROBLEM: How much work is done on a 16 N sack of potatoes when you lift the sack 1.5 m?

$$W = 16 \text{ N} \times 1.5 \text{ m}$$
$$W = \mathbf{24\ J}$$

Work It Out!

Based on what you know about work, answer the following questions. Be sure to show your work.

1. A deflated hot-air balloon weighs a total of 8000 N. Filled with hot air, the balloon rises to a height of 1000 m. How much work is accomplished by the hot air?

____

____

2. A rope is thrown over a beam, and one end is tied to a 300 N bundle of lumber. You pull the free end of the rope 2 m with a force of 400 N to lift the lumber off the ground. How much work have you done?

____

____

3. A 150 N boy rides a 60 N bicycle a total of 200 m at a constant speed. The frictional force against the forward motion of the bicycle equals 35 N. How much work does the boy do? Explain your answer. (Hint: Remember that work is only done when the motion is in the same direction that the force is applied.)

____

____

____

____

Name ________________ Date ________ Class ________

Part 2: Work and Power

Work is closely related to the concept of power. **Power** is a measure of how much work is done in a certain time. The faster work is done, the more power is produced.

EQUATION:

$$\text{power} = \frac{\text{work}}{\text{time}}$$

$$P = \frac{W}{t}$$

The unit for power is the **watt (W).** One watt (W) is equal to 1 J of work done for 1 second. Use the data given in the diagram below to determine how much work and power are involved in each step. Remember to show your work.

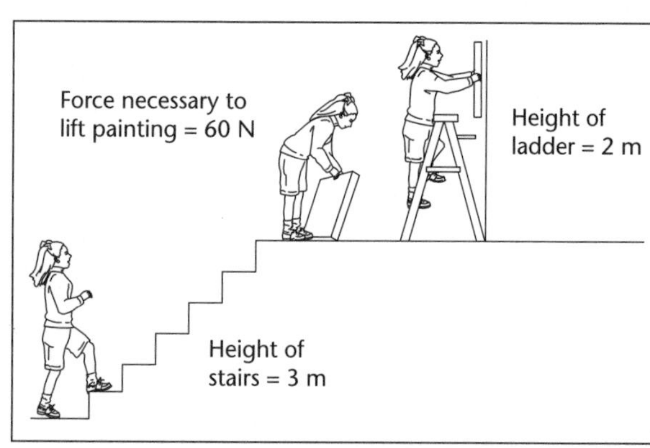

Step 1: A 50 N girl climbs the flight of stairs in 3 seconds.

Work = ________________

____

Power = ________________

____

Step 2: The girl lifts a painting to a height of 0.5 m in 0.75 seconds.

Work= ________________

____

Power= ________________

____

Step 3: The girl climbs the ladder with the painting in 5 seconds.

Work= ________________

____

Power= ________________

____

Challenge Yourself!

4. A crane lifts a load of steel that weighs 9.3×10^5 N a distance of 100 m. It takes 5 minutes to complete the task.

a. How much work is done by the crane?

____

b. How much power does the crane produce?

____

Name ______________________ Date ____________ Class ____________

WORKSHEET

52 MATH IN SCIENCE: PHYSICAL SCIENCE

MATH SKILLS USED
Multiplication
Division
Decimals
Geometry

A Bicycle Trip

Use your math skills to see how the gears of a bicycle transfer energy.

The gears on a bicycle make up a system for transferring energy from the rider's legs to the front sprockets (or gears) and then through the chain to the rear wheel. The 12-speed bicycle below has two front sprockets (*A*) connected to the pedals. The sprockets contain 42 and 52 teeth, respectively. The rear wheel has a diameter of 70 cm. It has six different-sized sprockets (*B*) attached at the center containing 14, 17, 20, 23, 26, and 28 teeth, going from the smallest to the largest sprocket. Front and rear *derailleurs* transfer the chain from one sprocket to another during the process of changing gears. The length of the pedal arm is 15 cm.

Sample Situation

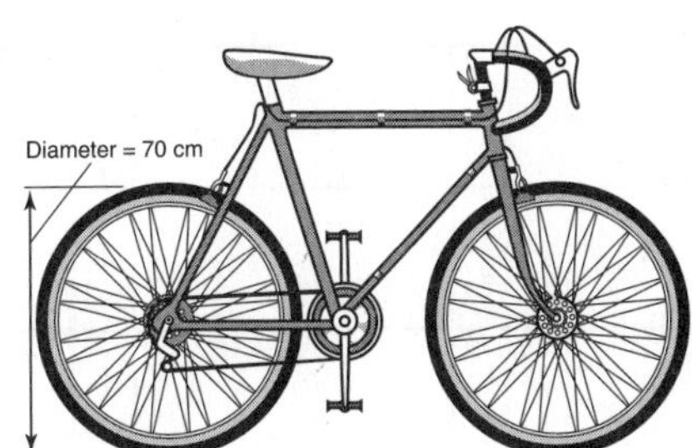

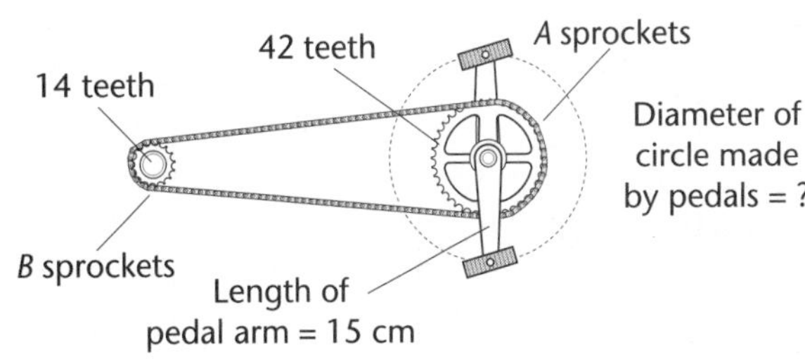

Use What You Know!

Suppose the chain is connected to the smaller sprocket in front, which contains 42 teeth, and to the smallest sprocket in the rear, which contains 14 teeth. Use the sample situation to answer the following questions:

1. When the pedals make one complete rotation, how many teeth in the front sprocket does the chain move over?

____

2. How many times will the rear sprocket and rear wheel turn during one rotation of the pedals?

____

3. a. What distance will each foot move during one complete turn (rotation) of the pedals? (*Hint:* circumference = 3.14 × diameter)

____

b. What distance will the rear wheel and bicycle move forward while the pedals make one complete turn?

____

4. How many times farther will the rear wheel of the bicycle move compared with the distance the rider's feet moved?

____

5. Using the sample situation from the previous page, fill out the following table:

	Teeth in A	Teeth in B	Wheel turns per pedal turn	Distance (cm) bicycle wheel moves per pedal turn	Distance (cm) pedals move per turn	Ratio of wheel distance to pedal distance
Smallest *A* connected to largest *B*	42	28				
Smallest *A* connected to second largest *B*		26				
Smallest *A* connected to third largest *B*		23				
Smallest *A* connected to fourth largest *B*						
Smallest *A* connected to fifth largest *B*						
Smallest *A* connected to smallest *B* (sample from previous page)			42 ÷ 14 = 3	3 × (3.14 × 70) = 659.4	30 × 3.14 = 94.2	659.4 ÷ 94.2 = 7
Largest *A* connected to largest *B*	52					
Largest *A* connected to second largest *B*						
Largest *A* connected to third largest *B*						
Largest *A* connected to fourth largest *B*		20				
Largest *A* connected to fifth largest *B*		17				
Largest *A* connected to smallest *B*		14				

Challenge Yourself!

6. Which *A* sprocket connected to which *B* sprocket will achieve the greatest distance?

____

7. What arrangement of the gears will give the least multiplication of the distance?

____

Name ______________________ Date __________ Class __________

WORKSHEET

MATH SKILLS USED
Division
Decimals

53 **MATH IN SCIENCE: PHYSICAL SCIENCE**

Mechanical Advantage

Use the equation for mechanical advantage to see how machines multiply force.

The **mechanical advantage** of a machine is the factor by which the machine multiplies force. The mechanical advantage of a machine can be used to determine how well a machine works and whether it can perform a particular job.

EQUATION: $$\text{mechanical advantage } (MA) = \frac{\text{output force}}{\text{input force}}$$

SAMPLE PROBLEM: What is the mechanical advantage of a lever that requires an input force of 20 N and lifts an object that weighs 60 N?

$$\text{mechanical advantage } (MA) = \frac{60 \text{ N}}{20 \text{ N}}$$

$$MA = \mathbf{3}$$

Practice Your Skills!

Use the equation for mechanical advantage to answer the following questions:

1. Amanda uses a wheelbarrow to lift a load of bricks. The bricks weigh 600 N, which is more than Amanda could normally carry. However, with the wheelbarrow, Amanda can lift the bricks with as little as 120 N. What is the mechanical advantage of the wheelbarrow?

   ____

2. Marshall wants to remove a tree stump from the ground. To do this, he puts one end of a long beam under the stump and puts all of his weight on the other end. His weight is just enough to lift the stump. The stump weighs 400 N. Marshall weighs 250 N. What is the mechanical advantage of the lever Marshall is using?

   ____

3. A system of pulleys allows a mechanic to lift an 1800 N engine.
   a. If the mechanic exerts a force of 600 N on the pulley system, what is the mechanical advantage of the machine?

      ____

   b. What is the mechanical advantage of the pulley system if the mechanic must exert 800 N of force to lift the engine?

      ____

   c. After improving the design of his pulley system, the mechanic can now lift the engine with a *MA* of 4. How much force is now required to lift the engine?

      ____

Name ______________________ Date ____________ Class ____________

WORKSHEET

54 **MATH IN SCIENCE: PHYSICAL SCIENCE**

MATH SKILLS USED
Multiplication Scientific Notation SI Measurement and Conversion

Color at Light Speed

Analyze the wavelength and frequency of the colors in light.

Visible light consists of a range of different colors that combine to form white light. This range is called the **color spectrum.** Each color in the color spectrum has a unique wavelength and frequency. Our eyes see light of different wavelengths as different colors. The frequency (f) and wavelength (λ) of visible light can be used to determine the speed of light (v) by the following equation:

$$\text{speed of light} = \text{frequency} \times \text{wavelength}$$

$$v = f \times \lambda$$

The frequency of waves is measured in waves per second, or hertz (Hz). The wavelength can be measured as the distance between two wave crests. The diagram below shows the spectrum of visible light with the corresponding wavelengths for each color. As you can see, the wavelengths of visible light fall in the range of 400 nanometers (nm) to 750 nm. One nanometer is equal to 0.000000001 m.

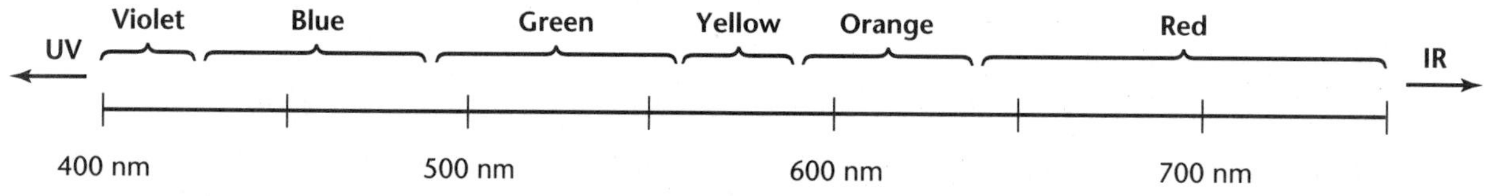

1. Calculate the speed of light for the following. Show your work.

a. a shade of yellow light with a wavelength of 5.8×10^{-7} m and a frequency of 5.17×10^{14} Hz

____

____

b. a shade of red light with a wavelength of 6.98×10^{-7} m and a frequency of 4.3×10^{14} Hz

____

____

c. a shade of violet light with a wavelength of 4×10^{-6} m and a frequency of 7.5×10^{13} Hz

____

____

d. What can you conclude about the speed of light of different colors?

____

____

2. a. If the speed of light is constant (meaning it does not change), does the wavelength increase or decrease with an increase in frequency?

____

b. What happens to the wavelength as the frequency decreases?

____

3. Convert the following metric measurements:

a. An orange light with a wavelength of 620 nm is ______________ m long.

b. A blue light with a wavelength of ______________ nm is 0.000445 mm long.

c. A ______________ light with a wavelength of ______________ nm is 0.00041 cm long.

d. A ______________ light with a wavelength of 550 nm is

______________ m long.

4. The relationship between the energy of a light wave and its frequency is given in the following equation:

$$E = h \times f$$

In this equation, f is the frequency and h is a constant.

a. Which of the colors from question 1 has the most energy?

____

b. Which color has the least energy?

____

c. What is the relationship between the frequency of a light wave and its energy?

____

d. What is the relationship between the wavelength of a light wave and its energy?

____

Name ______________________ Date ____________ Class ____________

STUDENT SELF-ASSESSMENT REVISITED

Go back and read your assessment on page vi. Then fill in the chart below.

Math skill	Good	OK	Needs improvement
Addition			
Subtraction			
Multiplication			
Division			
Positive and negative numbers			
Fractions			
Ratios and proportions			
Decimals			
Percentages			
Powers of 10			
Scientific notation			
SI measurement and conversion			
Dimensional analysis			
Geometry			

Describe three instances in which you have needed to use math in your science class.

____

____

Which of your math skills have improved the most? Which need more improvement?

____

____

____

Art Credits

All art, unless otherwise noted, by Holt, Rinehart and Winston.

Abbreviated as follows: (t) top; (b) bottom; (l) left; (r) right; (c) center; (bkgd) background.

Front Cover (zebra), JH Pete Carmichael/Getty Images; (arch), Steve Niedirf Photography/Getty Images; (aircraft), Creatas/PictureQuest; (owl), Kim Taylor/Bruce Coleman Page 15 (cl), Layne Lundstrom; 15 (c), Laurie O'Keefe; 15 (cr), Kiwi Studios; 41 (tr), Accurate Art, Inc.; 42 (tl), Accurate Art, Inc.; 42 (tc), Accurate Art, Inc.; 42 (tr), Accurate Art, Inc.; 42 (cl), Accurate Art, Inc.; 42 (c), Accurate Art, Inc.; 42 (cr), Accurate Art, Inc.; 42 (bl), Accurate Art, Inc.; 42 (br), Accurate Art, Inc.; 43 (tl), Accurate Art, Inc.; 43 (tr), Accurate Art, Inc.; 43 (cl), Accurate Art, Inc.; 43 (cr), Accurate Art, Inc.; 43 (bl), Accurate Art, Inc.; 43 (br), Accurate Art, Inc.; 71 (tl), Accurate Art, Inc.; 71 (tc), Accurate Art, Inc.; 71 (tr), Accurate Art, Inc.; 71 (c), Kiwi Studios; 72 (tr), Layne Lundstrom; 72 (br), Accurate Art, Inc.; 74 (br), Accurate Art, Inc.; 75 (cl), Thomas Kennedy; 75 (bl), Kiwi Studios; 75 (bl), Kiwi Studios; 80 (cl), Thomas Kennedy; 81 (cl), Kiwi Studios; 81 (cr), Accurate Art, Inc.

Answer Key

Math Skills

▪ CONTENTS ▪

Math Skills	**87**
Math in Science: Integrated Science	**110**
Math in Science: Life Science	**114**
Math in Science: Earth Science	**118**
Math in Science: Physical Science	**123**

Name ______________ Date ________ Class ________

WORKSHEET 1 MATH SKILLS

Addition Review

Addition is used to find the total of two or more quantities. The answer to an addition problem is known as the *sum*.

PROCEDURE: To find the sum of a set of numbers, align the numbers vertically so that the ones digits are in the same column. Add each column, working from right to left.

SAMPLE PROBLEM: Find the sum of 317, 435, and 92.

Step 1: Add the ones. Don't forget to carry your numbers.	**Step 2:** Add the tens.	**Step 3:** Add the hundreds.
1 317 435 + 92 4	1 1 317 435 + 92 44	1 317 435 + 92 844

The sum is **844.**

Add It Up!

1. Find the sums of the following problems:

a.	**b.**	**c.**	**d.**
348 + 21	98,125 + 233	593 + 386	36,186 + 27,309
369	98,358	979	63,495

2. Your doctor advises you to take 60 mg of vitamin C, 20 mg of niacin, and 15 mg of zinc every day. How many milligrams of nutrients will you take?

60 mg + 20 mg + 15 mg = 95 mg

3. A chemistry experiment calls for 356 mL of water, 197 mL of saline solution, and 55 mL of vinegar. How much liquid is needed in all?

356 mL + 197 mL + 55 mL = 608 mL

4. Between 1980 and 1992, the population of San Bernardino County, CA, increased by 639,327 people. If the population in 1980 was 895,016, what was the population in 1992?

895,016 + 639,327 = 1,534,343

5. Halley's comet returns to our solar system every 76 years. Its last visit was in 1986. What year will it appear again?

1986 + 76 = 2062

Name ______________ Date ________ Class ________

WORKSHEET 2 MATH SKILLS

Subtraction Review

Subtraction is used to take one number from another number. The answer to a subtraction problem is known as the *difference*. The difference is how much larger or smaller one number is than the other.

PROCEDURE: To find the difference between two numbers, first align the numbers vertically so that the ones digits are in the same column, with the larger number above the smaller number. Subtract, working from right to left, one column at a time. Remember to borrow when necessary.

SAMPLE PROBLEM: Find the difference between 622 and 348.

Step 1: Subtract the ones, borrowing when necessary.	**Step 2:** Subtract the tens, borrowing when necessary.	**Step 3:** Subtract the hundreds.
62¹**2** − 34⁵**8** **4**	6¹**2**¹2 − 3⁴**4**⁵8 **7** 4	**6**¹2¹2 − **3**⁴4⁵8 **2** 7 4

The difference of the numbers is **274**.

Take It Away!

1. Find the difference in the following problems:

   a. 88 − 36 = 52
   b. 1695 − 352 = 1343
   c. 47,220 − 36,195 = 11,025
   d. 6048 − 3724 = 2324

2. 571 − 338 = 233

3. 8317 − 211 = 8106

4. Mars has a diameter of 6790 km. The diameter of Jupiter is 142,984 km. How much larger is the diameter of Jupiter than the diameter of Mars?

   142,984 km − 6790 km = 136,194 km

5. A horse is born with a mass of 36 kg. It is expected to have a mass of 495 kg when fully grown. How much mass will it gain?

   495 kg − 36 kg = 459 kg

6. Traveling with the wind, a plane reaches a speed of 212 m/s. On the return trip, the same plane flies into the wind and achieves a speed of only 179 m/s. How much faster does the plane fly with the wind?

   212 m/s − 179 m/s = 33 m/s

Name ______________ Date ________ Class ________

WORKSHEET 3 MATH SKILLS

Multiplying Whole Numbers

Suppose every student in your class planted 5 seeds in your school's garden. How many seeds were planted? You could repeatedly add 5 seeds plus 5 seeds until every student's seeds had been added, but this would be pretty time consuming. **Multiplication**, which simplifies addition, is the process of calculating the total of a number that is added together a specific number of times. For example, 3 × 4 means adding 3 together 4 times, or 3 + 3 + 3 + 3 = 12. So 3 × 4 = 12. The answer to a multiplication problem is called the *product*.

PROCEDURE: To find the product of two whole numbers, align your numbers so that the ones digits are in the same column. Multiply each digit of the top number by the ones digit in the bottom number, carrying when necessary. Then multiply each digit in the top number by the tens in the bottom number, regrouping when necessary. Finally, add the partial products to find the final product.

SAMPLE PROBLEM: Find the product of 34 and 16.

Step 1: Align the numbers vertically. Multiply each digit in the top number by the ones digit in the bottom number. Carry when necessary.	**Step 2:** Multiply each digit in the top number by the tens in the bottom number. Imagine adding a zero in the ones column as a place holder.	**Step 3:** Add the partial products.
²**34** × **16** **204**	**34** × **16** 204 **34**0	34 × 16 **204** + **34**0 **544**

The product is **544**.

Practice Your Skills!

1. Multiply. Don't forget to show all your work.

   a. 12 × 24: 48, 24 → 288
   b. 245 × 36: 1470, 735 → 8820
   c. 46 × 87: 322, 368 → 4002
   d. 2751 × 11: 2751, 2751 → 30,261

2. A farm produces 864 bushels of corn per square kilometer. The farmer plants 127 km² of corn. How many bushels of corn will the farm produce?

   864 bushels/km² × 127 km² = 109,728 bushels

3. A bee travels 147 m one way from its hive to the garden. If the bee makes 93 round trips between the hive and the garden, how far will it have traveled? Be careful!

   147 m/one-way trip × 2 one-way trips/round trip = 294 m/round trip;
   294 m/round trip × 93 round trips = 27,342 m

Copyright © by Holt, Rinehart and Winston. All rights reserved.

Name ______________ Date ______________ Class ______________

WORKSHEET

4 MATH SKILLS

A Shortcut for Multiplying Large Numbers

Imagine that you are a doctor doing research on white blood cells. You know that there are approximately 80,000 white blood cells in 1 mL of blood. You have a sample of 50 mL of blood. How many white blood cells are in the sample? You could multiply to find the answer, of course, but it's a large number and you need an answer quickly. How can you make this easier? Read on to learn an easy way to find the product of large numbers.

PROCEDURE: To find the product of large numbers, remove the zeros at the end of one or both numbers. Next, multiply the non-zero numbers. Finally, at the end of the product, replace the same number of zeros that you removed from your multipliers.

SAMPLE PROBLEM: Multiply 80,000 by 50.

Step 1: Remove the zeros from the end of your numbers, and multiply the non-zero numbers.

80,000 → 8~~0,000~~ → 8
50 → 5~~0~~ → × 5
40

Step 2: At the end of your product, replace the total number of zeros you removed from the multipliers. Because you removed a total of five zeros from your multipliers, place five zeros after your product.

80,000 × 50 = 4,**000,000**

It's Your Turn!

Using the method above, find the products of the following problems, and write the corresponding letter from the correct answer on the line.

1. 300 × 90,000 ___C___ **A.** 31,720,000
2. 45 × 8500 ___E___ **B.** 3,524,000
3. 4400 × 7500 ___D___ **C.** 27,000,000
4. 52,000 × 610 ___A___ **D.** 33,000,000
5. 88,100 × 40 ___B___ **E.** 382,500

Challenge Yourself!

A super-fast chess computer can perform 200,000,000 calculations per second. How many calculations can it perform in the 3 minutes it is allowed for each move?

3 minutes × 60 seconds/minute = 180 seconds;

2~~00,000,000~~ calculations/second × 18~~0~~ seconds = 36 → 36,000,000,000 calculations

Name ______________ Date ______________ Class ______________

WORKSHEET

5 MATH SKILLS

Dividing Whole Numbers with Long Division

Long division, which is used to divide numbers of more than one digit, is really just a series of simple division, multiplication, and subtraction problems. The number that you divide is called the *dividend*. The number you divide the dividend by is the *divisor*. The answer to a division problem is called a *quotient*.

SAMPLE PROBLEM: Divide 564 by 12, or $12\overline{)564}$.

Step 1: Because you cannot divide 12 into 5, you must start by dividing 12 into 56. To do this, ask yourself, "What number multiplied by 12 comes closest to 56 without going over?" 4 × 12 = 48, so place a 4 in the quotient.

$$\begin{array}{r} 4 \\ 12\overline{)564} \end{array}$$

Step 2: Multiply the 4 by the divisor and place the product under the 56. Then subtract that product from 56.

$$\begin{array}{r} 4 \\ 12\overline{)564} \\ -48 \\ \hline 8 \end{array}$$

Step 3: Bring the next digit down from the dividend (4), and divide this new number (84) by the divisor, as you did in Step 1. Because 12 divides into 84 seven times, write 7 in the quotient.

$$\begin{array}{r} 47 \\ 12\overline{)564} \\ -48\downarrow \\ \hline 84 \\ -84 \\ \hline 0 \end{array}$$

The quotient is **47.**

Divide It Up!

1. Fill in the blanks in the following long-division problems:

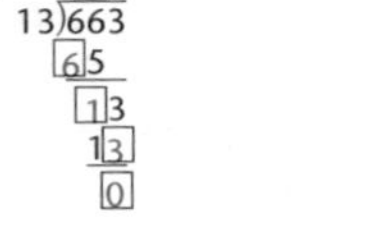

a. $13\overline{)663}$ = 51; 65; 13; 13; 0

b. $9\overline{)918}$ = 102; 9; 01; 0; 18; 18; 0

c. $17\overline{)408}$ = 24; 34; 68; 68; 0

2. Complete the following long-division problems on a separate sheet of paper:

a. 3575 ÷ 11 = ___325___ **b.** $52\overline{)1664}$ = ___32___

c. $3\overline{)2940}$ = ___980___ **d.** 4630 ÷ 5 = ___926___

Name ____________ Date ________ Class ________

WORKSHEET 6 **MATH SKILLS**

Checking Division with Multiplication

Multiplication and division "undo" one another. This means that when you ask yourself, "What is 12 divided by 3?" it is the same as asking, "What number *multiplied* by 3 gives 12?" You can use this method to catch mistakes in your division.

PROCEDURE: To check your division with multiplication, multiply the quotient of your division problem by the divisor and compare the result with the dividend. If they are equal, your division was correct.

SAMPLE PROBLEM 1: Divide 564 by 47, and check your result with multiplication.

Step 1: Divide to find your quotient.	**Step 2:** Multiply the quotient by the divisor.	**Step 3:** Compare the product with your dividend.
12 47)564 −47 94 −94 0	12 × 47 84 48 564	**564** = **564** Correct!

Check It Out!

Complete the following divisions, and check your math by multiplying the quotient by your divisor. Are the product and the dividend equal?

1. 15)405 = 27
30
105
105
0

quotient × *divisor*: 27 × 15

quotient = 27 product = 405

2. 14)1694 = 121
14
29
28
14
14
0

quotient × *divisor*: 121 × 14

quotient = 121 product = 1694

3. 12)252 = 21
24
12
12
0

quotient × *divisor*: 21 × 12

quotient = 21 product = 252

Name ____________ Date ________ Class ________

WORKSHEET 7 **MATH SKILLS**

What Is an Average?

Suppose that your class is doing an experiment to determine the boiling point of a particular liquid. Working in groups, your classmates come up with several answers that are all slightly different. Your teacher asks you to determine which temperature best represents all of the varying results from the class. A mathematical tool called an **average**, or *mean*, will help you solve the problem. An average allows you to simplify a list of numbers into a single number that *approximates* the value of all of them. Check it out!

PROCEDURE: To calculate the average of any set of numbers, first add all of the numbers to find the sum. Then divide the sum by the amount of numbers in your set. The result is the average of your numbers.

SAMPLE PROBLEM: Find the average of the following set of numbers:

5, 4, 7, 8

Step 1: Find the sum.

$$5 + 4 + 7 + 8 = \mathbf{24}$$

Step 2: Divide the sum by the amount of numbers in your set. Because there are four numbers in your set, divide the sum by 4.

$$24 \div 4 = 6 \text{ or } \frac{24}{4} = \mathbf{6}$$

The average of the numbers is **6.**

Practice Your Skills!

Be sure to show your work for the following problems:

1. Find the average of each of the following sets of numbers.

a. 19 m, 11 m, 29 m, 62 m, 14 m

19 m + 11 m + 29 m + 62 m + 14 m = 135 m; 135 m ÷ 5 = 27 m

b. 12 cm, 16 cm, 25 cm, 15 cm

12 cm + 16 cm + 25 cm + 15 cm = 68 cm; 68 cm ÷ 4 = 17 cm

c. 31°C, 42°C, 35°C, 38°C, 59°C

31°C + 42°C + 35°C + 38°C + 59°C = 205°C; 205°C ÷ 5 = 41°C

Name ______ Date ______ Class ______

What Is an Average? continued

Use the data in the tables to complete the following problems. Be sure to show your work.

Height of Students (cm)

Students	Grade 6	Grade 7	Grade 8	Grade 9
Gretchen	152	156	159	163
Dylan	151	152	157	162
Sergio	144	147	150	152

2. Calculate the average of Gretchen's and Dylan's heights in the 8th grade.

159 cm + 157 cm = 316 cm; 316 cm ÷ 2 = 158 cm

3. What is the average height of all three students in Grade 6?

152 cm + 151 cm + 144 cm = 447 cm; 447 cm ÷ 3 = 149 cm

Number of Wildfires in 1993–1996

Year	Arizona	New Mexico	Oklahoma	Texas
1993	10	7	17	85
1994	16	11	24	84
1995	12	5	7	72
1996	13	5	37	91

4. What was the average number of wildfires to occur annually in New Mexico for the years 1993–1996?

7 + 11 + 5 + 5 = 28; 28 ÷ 4 = 7

5. What was the average number of wildfires for all four states in 1995?

12 + 5 + 7 + 72 = 96; 96 ÷ 4 = 24

6. What was the average number of wildfires to occur annually in Texas for the years 1993–1996?

85 + 84 + 72 + 91 = 332; 332 ÷ 4 = 83

Name ______ Date ______ Class ______

WORKSHEET 8 MATH SKILLS

Average, Mode, and Median

Although an average, or mean, is the most common way to simplify a list of numbers, there are other mathematical tools that can help you work with lists of numbers. **Mode** is the number or value that appears most often in a particular set of numbers. **Median** is the number that falls in the *numerical center* of a list of numbers. Read on to find out how to find mode and median.

PROCEDURE: *To find the mode,* list your numbers in numerical order. Then determine which number appears most often in the set. That number is the mode. **Note:** A list of numbers may have more than one mode. If no number appears more often than the others, that series of numbers does not have a mode.

SAMPLE PROBLEM: Find the mode of 4, 3, 6, 10, and 3.

Step 1: List the numbers in numerical order.

3, 3, 4, 6, 10

Step 2: Determine the number that appears most often in the set.

3, 3, 4, 6, 10

The mode of 4, 3, 6, 10, and 3 is **3.**

PROCEDURE: *To find the median,* list the numbers in numerical order. Next determine the number that appears in the middle of the set. **Note:** If more than one number falls in the middle, the median is the average of those numbers.

SAMPLE PROBLEM: Find the median of 25, 22, 24, 19, 25, 14, 26, and 15.

Step 1: List the numbers in numerical order.

14, 15, 19, 22, 24, 25, 25, 26

Step 2: Determine which number falls in the middle of the set.

14, 15, 19, 22, 24, 25, 25, 26

Because two numbers fall in the middle (22 and 24), the median is their average.

Median = (22 + 24) ÷ 2 = **23**

Get in the Mode!

1. Find the mode and median for the following sets of numbers:

a. 37, 30, 35, 37, 32, 40, 34

Mode 37 Median 35

b. 19, 29, 9, 12, 10

Mode none Median 12

c. 109, 84, 88, 107, 84, 94

Mode 84 Median 91

d. 26, 53, 39, 53, 49, 56, 35, 26

Mode 26; 53 Median 44

e. 25 m, 24 m, 27 m, 27 m, 49 m, 47 m, 45 m

Mode 27 m Median 27 m

f. 98 L, 99 L, 101 L, 111 L, 132 L, 103 L

Mode none Median 102 L

Name ______________ Date ______ Class ______

Peregrine Falcons—How Fast Can They Fly?

The peregrine falcon is the fastest bird in the world. It can reach speeds of almost 300 km/h when hunting. An ornithologist, a scientist who studies birds, has gathered the data in the chart below to try to learn exactly how fast the falcons can fly. Use what you have learned about averages, modes, and medians to analyze some of the birds' top speeds.

Falcon Flight Speeds*

Day	Falcon A	Falcon B	Falcon C	Falcon D	Falcon E
1	189	199	211	253	199
2	275	261	241	235	279
3	262	225	271	190	271
4	203	199	223	185	265
5	241	227	209	199	253
6	222	240	265	253	232
7	203	203	240	260	279

*All flight speeds are in km/h.

2. What was the average top speed of Falcon B for the entire week?

199 + 261 + 225 + 199 + 227 + 240 + 203 = 1554; 1554 ÷ 7 = 222 km/h

3. What were the modes for Falcon D and Falcon E for the entire week?

Falcon D: 185, 190, 199, 235, 253, 253, 260. The mode was 253 km/h.

Falcon E: 199, 232, 253, 265, 271, 279, 279. The mode was 279 km/h.

4. Which had a faster median speed for the week, Falcon A or Falcon B?

Falcon A: 189, 203, 203, 222, 241, 262, 275; The median was 222.

Falcon B: 199, 199, 203, 225, 227, 240, 261; The median was 225.

Falcon B had the faster median speed.

5. What were the median speeds for Falcon B and Falcon D for days 1–6?

Falcon B: 199, 199, 225, 227, 240, 261; (225 + 227) ÷ 2 = 226 km/h

Falcon D: 185, 190, 199, 235, 253, 253; (199 + 235) ÷ 2 = 217 km/h

Name ______________ Date ______ Class ______

WORKSHEET 9 MATH SKILLS

Comparing Integers on a Number Line

An **integer** is any whole number (0, 1, 2, 3, . . .) or its opposite. A good way to compare integers is with a *number line,* which is used to represent positive and negative numbers in order. A number line looks like this:

−10 −9 −8 −7 −6 −5 −4 −3 −2 −1 0 1 2 3 4 5 6 7 8 9 10

The farther a number is to the right on a number line, the greater the number. The farther a number is to the left on a number line, the smaller the number.

PROCEDURE: To compare integers on a number line, simply place your values on the line, with positive numbers to the right of zero and negative numbers to the left of zero. The number that is the farthest to the right is the greatest number. The number that is the farthest to the left is the smallest number.

SAMPLE PROBLEM: Which is greater, −8 or −3?

Step 1: Draw your number line and select a point for 0. Then fill in the integer values on the line.

Step 2: Place the integers you are comparing on the number line. Because both numbers are negative, they will both be to the left of zero.

−10 −9 **−8** −7 −6 −5 −4 **−3** −2 −1 0 1 2 3 4 5 6 7 8 9 10

Because −3 is farther to the right than −8, **−3** is greater than −8.

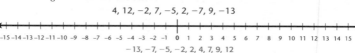

Practice Your Skills!

1. Locate the following integers on the number line. Then list them in order from smallest to greatest on the line below.

4, 12, −2, 7, −5, 2, −7, 9, −13

−15 −14 −13 −12 −11 −10 −9 −8 −7 −6 −5 −4 −3 −2 −1 0 1 2 3 4 5 6 7 8 9 10 11 12 13 14 15

−13, −7, −5, −2, 2, 4, 7, 9, 12

2. Use a number line to correctly place the sign > (greater than) or < (less than) between the numbers in each of the following pairs.

a. 89 __<__ 98 **b.** −89 __>__ −98 **c.** −98 __<__ −69

3. This table shows estimates of the mean temperatures on the surface of nine planets. List the planets on the line below in order from hottest to coldest.

Earth	Jupiter	Mars	Mercury	Neptune	Pluto	Saturn	Uranus	Venus
8°C	−150°C	−37°C	179°C	−225°C	−236°C	−185°C	−214°C	453°C

Venus, Mercury, Earth, Mars, Jupiter, Saturn, Uranus, Neptune, Pluto

Name ______________________ Date __________ Class __________

WORKSHEET

10 MATH SKILLS

Arithmetic with Positive and Negative Numbers

The **absolute value** of a number is its distance from zero on the number line. For example, −7 (a negative number) and 7 (a positive number) are the same distance from zero on the number line, and both have an absolute value of 7. Using absolute values simplifies the process of doing arithmetic with positive and negative numbers.

1. Find the absolute value of the following numbers:

a. −7 ___7___ **b.** 14 ___14___

c. 325,000 ___325,000___ **d.** −475 ___475___

e. 230 ___230___ **f.** −52 ___52___

Part 1: Adding Positive and Negative Numbers

PROCEDURE: Determine if you are adding numbers that have the same or different signs. Then follow the appropriate set of directions below.

Adding same signs	Example −3 + (−5)	Adding opposite signs	Example −3 + 5
Step 1: Add their absolute values.	3 + 5 = 8	**Step 1:** Subtract the smaller absolute value from the larger.	5 − 3 = 2
Step 2: Make the sign of the answer the same as the sign of the orig-inal numbers.	Because −3 and −5 are both negative, the answer will be negative. **Answer:** −3 + (−5) = −8	**Step 2:** Choose the sign of the number with the greater absolute value.	Because 5 has a greater absolute value than 3, and 5 is positive, your answer will also be positive. **Answer:** −3 + 5 = 2

Add It Up!

2. Complete the following equations. When finished, go back and check your signs.

a. 14 + (−17) = ___17 − 14 = 3; −3___ **b.** −9 + (−23) = ___9 + 23 = 32; −32___

c. −16 + 21 = ___21 − 16 = 5; 5___ **d.** −12 + 12 = ___12 − 12 = 0; 0___

e. 15 + (−4) = ___15 − 4 = 11; 11___ **f.** −7 + (−7) = ___7 + 7 = 14; −14___

Name ______________________ Date __________ Class __________

Part 2: Subtracting Positive and Negative Numbers

PROCEDURE: To subtract integers, find the opposite of the number you are subtracting. Then *add* this opposite to the number you are subtracting from. The result is your answer.

SAMPLE PROBLEM: −3 − (−5) = ___?___

Step 1: Find the opposite of the number you want to subtract.

The opposite of −5 is 5.

Step 2: Add this opposite to the number you are subtracting from.

− 3 − (−5) = −3 + 5 = **2**

Take It Away!

3. Complete the following subtraction problems. Remember to check your work.

a. 5 − (−7) = ___7; 5 + 7 = 12___ **b.** −11 − 5 = ___−5; −11 + (−5) = −16___

c. −1 − 1 = ___−1; −1 + (−1) = −2___ **d.** 22 − (−8) = ___8; 22 + 8 = 30___

e. 14 − (−3) = ___3; 14 + 3 = 17___ **f.** −9 − 4 = ___−4; −9 + (−4) = −13___

Part 3: Multiplying and Dividing Positive and Negative Numbers

PROCEDURE: To multiply or divide two integers, multiply or divide their absolute values. Then apply the following rule to determine if the answer is positive or negative:

- The product or quotient of two *same-sign* numbers is *positive*.
- The product or quotient of two *opposite-sign* numbers is *negative*.

SAMPLE PROBLEM A: −7 × 11 = ___?___

Step 1: Multiply the absolute values to find the absolute value of the product.

7 × 11 = 77

Step 2: Apply the rule of signs: Because you are finding the product of *opposite-sign* numbers, the product will be *negative*.

− 7 × 11 = **−77**

SAMPLE PROBLEM B: −12 ÷ (−4) = ___?___

Step 1: Divide the absolute values to find the absolute value of the quotient.

12 ÷ 4 = 3

Step 2: Apply the rule of signs: Because you are finding the quotient of *same-sign* numbers, the quotient will be *positive*.

−12 ÷ (−4) = **3**

Name ______________________ Date __________ Class __________

Arithmetic with Positive and Negative Numbers, continued

Challenge Yourself: Multiply Your Way up the Pyramid!

4. Each brick's number is the product of the two numbers under it. Starting on the bottom row, multiply to complete the empty bricks.

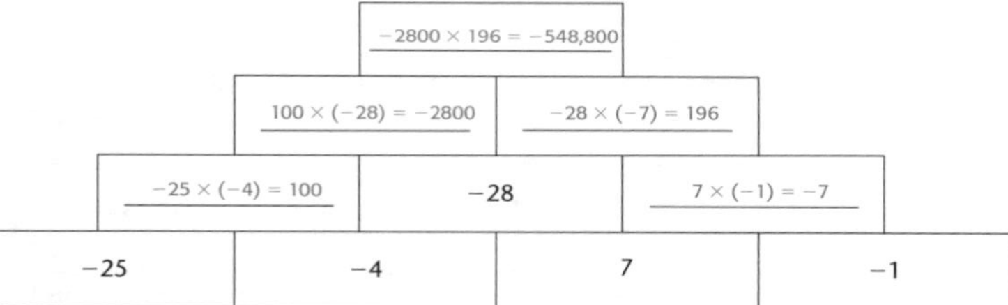

Divide Your Way down Again!

5. Each brick's number is the quotient of the two numbers above it. Starting from the top left brick, divide each brick by the number on its right side. Place the quotient in the empty brick below. Continue until all the bricks are filled.

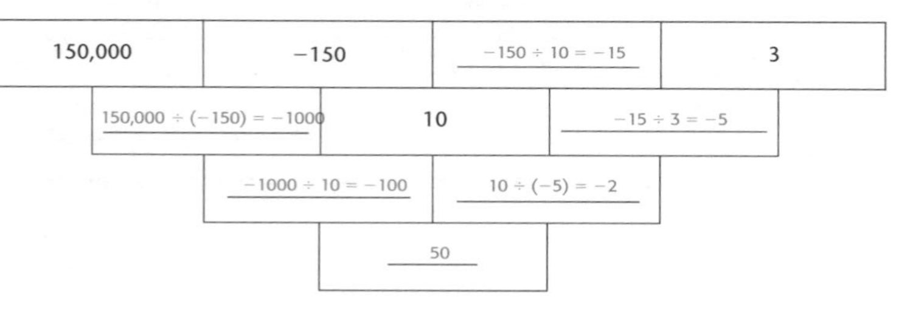

Name ______________________ Date __________ Class __________

WORKSHEET 11 MATH SKILLS

What Is a Fraction?

Suppose that you are doing an experiment in your class on the benefits of sunlight to plants. Your teacher has asked you to put $\frac{1}{2}$ of the plants in the sun. What does that mean? While whole numbers, such as 1 and 879, are used to indicate *how many*, **fractions** are used to tell *how much of a whole.*

The number below the fraction bar in a fraction is called the *denominator.* This number indicates how many parts there are in the whole. The number above the fraction bar, called the *numerator,* tells you how many parts of that whole are represented.

PROCEDURE: To make a fraction, write the total number of units in the whole as your denominator. Then write the number of parts of that whole being represented as the numerator.

SAMPLE PROBLEM: Your class has 24 plants. Your teacher instructs you to put 5 in a shady spot. What fraction does this represent?

Step 1: Write the total number of parts in the whole as the denominator.

$$\frac{\quad}{24}$$

Step 2: Write the number of parts of the whole being represented as the numerator.

$$\frac{5}{24}$$

$\frac{\mathbf{5}}{\mathbf{24}}$ of the plants will be in the shade.

Constructing Fractions

1. What fraction of the whole does the shaded or patterned part represent?

a. $\frac{2}{4}$

b. $\frac{5}{6}$

c. $\frac{2}{3}$

2. Of the 29 students in your class, 10 have brown hair, 8 have black hair, 6 have blond hair, and the rest have red hair.

a. What fraction of the class has blond hair? $\frac{6}{29}$

b. What fraction of the class has red hair? $\frac{29-10-8-6}{29} = \frac{5}{29}$

Name ______________________ Date ____________ Class ____________

WORKSHEET 12 MATH SKILLS

Reducing Fractions to Lowest Terms

Suppose you have the fraction $\frac{30}{45}$. Those are pretty big numbers to deal with. Is there a simpler way to write the same fraction? Well, one common method is to write the fraction in **lowest terms.** A fraction in lowest terms is written using the smallest numbers possible that have the same relationship as the numbers in the original fraction. A fraction in lowest terms is the simplest form of that fraction. Read on to learn how to reduce a fraction to lowest terms.

PROCEDURE: To reduce a fraction to lowest terms, first find all the numbers that divide evenly into the numerator and the denominator. These numbers are known as *factors.* Find the largest factor that is common to both the numerator and the denominator. This is known as the **Greatest Common Factor (GCF).** Then divide both the numerator and the denominator by the GCF.

SAMPLE PROBLEM: Reduce the fraction $\frac{30}{45}$ to lowest terms.

Step 1: Find all the factors of the numerator and denominator, and determine which is the largest factor in both lists, or the GCF.

factors of the numerator 30: 1, 2, 3, 5, 6, 10, **15**, 30
factors of the denominator 45: 1, 3, 5, 9, **15**, 45

Step 2: Divide both the numerator and the denominator by the GCF, which is 15.

$$\frac{30}{45} = \frac{30 \div 15}{45 \div 15} = \frac{2}{3}$$

$\frac{30}{45}$ reduced to lowest terms is $\mathbf{\frac{2}{3}}$.

How Low Can You Go?

1. Reduce each fraction to lowest terms.

a. $\frac{10}{12}$ $\frac{10 \div 2}{12 \div 2} = \frac{5}{6}$

b. $\frac{36}{60}$ $\frac{36 \div 12}{60 \div 12} = \frac{3}{5}$

c. $\frac{75}{100}$ $\frac{75 \div 25}{100 \div 25} = \frac{3}{4}$

d. $\frac{17}{68}$ $\frac{17 \div 17}{68 \div 17} = \frac{1}{4}$

e. $\frac{8}{64}$ $\frac{8 \div 8}{64 \div 8} = \frac{1}{8}$

f. $\frac{48}{54}$ $\frac{48 \div 6}{54 \div 6} = \frac{8}{9}$

g. $\frac{11}{15}$ $\frac{11}{15}$

h. $\frac{150}{200}$ $\frac{150 \div 50}{200 \div 50} = \frac{3}{4}$

2. Circle the fractions below that are already written in lowest terms.

a. $\frac{7}{77}$ (b.) $\frac{21}{25}$ (c.) $\frac{17}{19}$ (d.) $\frac{9}{20}$ (e.) $\frac{37}{51}$

Name ______________________ Date ____________ Class ____________

WORKSHEET 13 MATH SKILLS

Improper Fractions and Mixed Numbers

An **improper fraction** is a fraction whose numerator is greater than its denominator, such as $\frac{13}{5}$. An improper fraction can be changed to a **mixed number,** which is a whole number with a fraction, such as $2\frac{3}{5}$. Likewise, a mixed number can be changed to an improper fraction when it is necessary for doing mathematical operations with these numbers.

PROCEDURE: To change an improper fraction to a mixed number, divide the numerator by the denominator and write the quotient as the whole number. If there is a remainder, place it over the denominator to make the fraction of the mixed number.

SAMPLE PROBLEM A: Change $\frac{17}{5}$ to a mixed number.

Step 1: Divide the numerator by the denominator.

$17 \div 5 = 3$, remainder 2

Step 2: Write the quotient as the whole number, and put the remainder over the original denominator as the fraction.

$\frac{17}{5} = 3\frac{2}{5}$

PROCEDURE: To change a mixed number to an improper fraction, multiply the denominator of the fraction by the whole number. Then add that product to the numerator. Finally, write the sum over the denominator.

SAMPLE PROBLEM B: Change $4\frac{2}{3}$ to an improper fraction.

Step 1: Multiply the denominator by the whole number.

$3 \times 4 = 12$

Step 2: Add the product to the numerator, and write the sum over the denominator.

$12 + 2 = 14$ $4\frac{2}{3} = \frac{14}{3}$

1. Write True or False next to each equation.

a. $3\frac{1}{3} = \frac{9}{3}$ $(3 \times 3) + 1 = 10; \frac{10}{3} \neq \frac{9}{3}$; False

b. $\frac{23}{4} = 5\frac{3}{4}$ $(4 \times 5) + 3 = 23; \frac{23}{4} = \frac{23}{4}$; True

c. $\frac{25}{4} = 5\frac{1}{6}$ $(6 \times 5) + 1 = 31; \frac{25}{4} \neq \frac{31}{6}$; False

d. $9\frac{7}{10} = \frac{97}{10}$ $(10 \times 9) + 7 = 97; \frac{97}{10} = \frac{97}{10}$; True

2. Change each improper fraction to a mixed number, and change each mixed number to an improper fraction.

a. $\frac{16}{3} =$ $16 \div 3 = 5R1; 5\frac{1}{3}$

b. $6\frac{1}{3} =$ $(3 \times 6) + 1 = 19; \frac{19}{3}$

c. $3\frac{5}{8} =$ $(8 \times 3) + 5 = 29; \frac{29}{8}$

d. $\frac{27}{5} =$ $27 \div 5 = 5R2; 5\frac{2}{5}$

Name ________________ Date ________ Class ________

WORKSHEET 14 MATH SKILLS

Adding and Subtracting Fractions

Part 1: Adding and Subtracting Fractions with the Same Denominator

PROCEDURE: To add fractions with the same denominator, add the numerators and put the sum over the original denominator. To subtract fractions with the same denominator, subtract the numerators and put the difference over the original denominator.

SAMPLE PROBLEM A:

$$\frac{3}{5} + \frac{1}{5} = ?$$

Add the numerators, and put the sum over the original denominator:

$$\frac{3}{5} + \frac{1}{5} = \frac{3+1}{5} = \frac{4}{5}$$

SAMPLE PROBLEM B:

$$\frac{8}{11} - \frac{3}{11} = ?$$

Subtract the numerators and put the difference over the original denominator:

$$\frac{8}{11} - \frac{3}{11} = \frac{8-3}{11} = \frac{5}{11}$$

Practice What You've Learned!

1. Add and subtract to complete the following equations. Reduce your answers to lowest terms.

a. $\frac{9}{17} - \frac{6}{17} =$ $\frac{9-6}{17} = \frac{3}{17}$

b. $\frac{5}{24} + \frac{4}{24} =$ $\frac{5+4}{24} = \frac{9}{24} = \frac{9 \div 3}{24 \div 3} = \frac{3}{8}$

c. $\frac{5}{4} + \frac{3}{4} =$ $\frac{5+3}{4} = \frac{8}{4} = \frac{8 \div 4}{4 \div 4} = \frac{2}{1} = 2$

d. $\frac{16}{5} - \frac{2}{5} =$ $\frac{16-2}{5} = \frac{14}{5} = 2\frac{4}{5}$

Part 2: Adding and Subtracting Fractions with Different Denominators

Sometimes you have to add or subtract fractions that have different denominators. To do this, you first need to rewrite your fractions so that they DO have the same denominator. Figuring out the **least common denominator (LCD)** of your fractions is the first step.

PROCEDURE: To find the least common denominator of two fractions, find the least common multiple of the denominators. In other words, look at the multiples of the numbers, and find out which they have in common. The common multiple with the lowest value is your LCD.

SAMPLE PROBLEM: What is the LCD of $\frac{3}{4}$ and $\frac{2}{3}$?

Step 1: List the multiples of 4.

$(4 \times 1) = 4$, $(4 \times 2) = 8$, $(4 \times 3) = \mathbf{12}$, $(4 \times 4) = 16$, etc.

Step 2: List the multiples of 3.

$(3 \times 1) = 3$, $(3 \times 2) = 6$, $(3 \times 3) = 9$, $(3 \times 4) = \mathbf{12}$, etc.

The least common denominator of $\frac{3}{4}$ and $\frac{2}{3}$ is **12.**

Name ________________ Date ________ Class ________

Lower Away!

2. Find the least common denominators of the following fractions:

a. $\frac{3}{5}$ and $\frac{5}{4}$ $(5 \times 1) = 5$, $(5 \times 2) = 10$, $(5 \times 3) = 15$, $(5 \times 4) = 20$; $(4 \times 1) = 4$, $(4 \times 2) = 8$, $(4 \times 3) = 12$, $(4 \times 4) = 16$, $(4 \times 5) = 20$; The LCD is 20.

b. $\frac{7}{8}$ and $\frac{4}{3}$ $(8 \times 1) = 8$, $(8 \times 2) = 16$, $(8 \times 3) = 24$; $(3 \times 1) = 3$, $(3 \times 2) = 6$, $(3 \times 3) = 9$, $(3 \times 4) = 12$, $(3 \times 5) = 15$, $(3 \times 6) = 18$, $(3 \times 7) = 21$, $(3 \times 8) = 24$; The LCD is 24.

Part 3: Putting the LCD to Work

Now that you know how to find the LCD, you are all set to add and subtract fractions with different denominators. Follow the steps below to see how to use the LCD to add and subtract fractions with different denominators.

PROCEDURE: To add or subtract fractions with different denominators, first find the LCD of the two fractions. Then determine the factor that each denominator is of that LCD. Multiply both the numerator and the denominator by those factors so that the fractions have the same denominator. Then add or subtract the numerators.

SAMPLE PROBLEM: $\frac{1}{2} + \frac{2}{5} = ?$

Step 1: Find the LCD.

$(2 \times 1) = 2$, $(2 \times 2) = 4$, $(2 \times 3) = 6$, $(2 \times 4) = 8$, $(2 \times 5) = \mathbf{10}$, etc.
$(5 \times 1) = 5$, $(5 \times 2) = \mathbf{10}$, etc.
The LCD is **10.**

Step 2: Determine the factor that each denominator is of the LCD.

Because $2 \times \mathbf{5} = 10$, 5 is the factor of 2.
Because $5 \times \mathbf{2} = 10$, **2** is the factor of 5.

Step 3: Multiply the factors of the LCD by the fractions.

$$\frac{1}{2} = \frac{1 \times 5}{2 \times 5} = \frac{5}{10} \qquad \frac{2}{5} = \frac{2 \times 2}{5 \times 2} = \frac{4}{10}$$

Step 4: Add the fractions.

$$\frac{5}{10} + \frac{4}{10} = \mathbf{\frac{9}{10}}$$

Use Your Skills!

3. Add and subtract. Don't forget to reduce your answers to lowest terms.

a. $\frac{2}{9} + \frac{1}{6} =$ LCD of 9 and 6 is 18; $\frac{2 \times 2}{9 \times 2} + \frac{1 \times 3}{6 \times 3} = \frac{4}{18} + \frac{3}{18} = \frac{7}{18}$

b. $\frac{14}{15} - \frac{5}{6} =$ LCD of 15 and 6 is 30; $\frac{14 \times 2}{15 \times 2} - \frac{5 \times 5}{6 \times 5} = \frac{28}{30} - \frac{25}{30} = \frac{3}{30} = \frac{1}{10}$

c. $\frac{12}{25} + \frac{2}{5} =$ LCD of 25 and 5 is 25; $\frac{12 \times 1}{25 \times 1} + \frac{2 \times 5}{5 \times 5} = \frac{12}{25} + \frac{10}{25} = \frac{22}{25}$

d. $\frac{1}{2} - \frac{3}{11} =$ LCD of 2 and 11 is 22; $\frac{1 \times 11}{2 \times 11} - \frac{3 \times 2}{11 \times 2} = \frac{11}{22} - \frac{6}{22} = \frac{5}{22}$

Name ______________ Date ________ Class ________

WORKSHEET 15 MATH SKILLS

Multiplying and Dividing Fractions

Compared with adding and subtracting fractions, multiplying and dividing fractions is quite simple. Just follow the steps below to see how it is done.

PROCEDURE 1: *To multiply fractions,* multiply the numerators and the denominators together and reduce the fraction (if necessary).

SAMPLE PROBLEM A: $\frac{5}{9} \times \frac{7}{10} = ?$

Step 1: Multiply the numerators and denominators.

$\frac{5}{9} \times \frac{7}{10} = \frac{5 \times 7}{9 \times 10} = \frac{35}{90}$

Step 2: Reduce.

$\frac{35}{90} = \frac{35 \div 5}{90 \div 5} = \frac{7}{18}$

Answer:

$\frac{5}{9} \times \frac{7}{10} = \frac{7}{18}$

PROCEDURE 2: *To divide fractions,* switch the numerator and denominator of the divisor (the number you divide by) to make that fraction's *reciprocal.* Then multiply the fraction and the reciprocal, and reduce if necessary.

SAMPLE PROBLEM B: $\frac{5}{8} \div \frac{3}{2} = ?$

Step 1: Rewrite the divisor as its reciprocal.

$\frac{3}{2} \rightarrow \frac{2}{3}$

Step 2: Multiply the dividend by the reciprocal.

$\frac{5}{8} \times \frac{2}{3} = \frac{5 \times 2}{8 \times 3} = \frac{10}{24}$

Step 3: Reduce.

$\frac{10}{24} = \frac{10 \div 2}{24 \div 2} = \frac{5}{12}$

Practice Your Skills!

1. Multiply and divide to complete the equations. Give your answers in lowest terms.

 a. $\frac{2}{5} \times \frac{5}{6} =$ $\frac{2 \times 5}{5 \times 6} = \frac{10}{30} = \frac{1}{3}$

 b. $\frac{1}{2} \div \frac{3}{8} =$ $\frac{1}{2} \times \frac{8}{3} = \frac{1 \times 8}{2 \times 3} = \frac{8}{6} = 1\frac{1}{3}$

 c. $\frac{4}{5} \times \frac{7}{12} =$ $\frac{4 \times 7}{5 \times 12} = \frac{28}{60} = \frac{28 \div 4}{60 \div 4} = \frac{7}{15}$

 d. $1\frac{1}{2} \div \frac{3}{4} =$ $\frac{3}{2} \times \frac{4}{3} = \frac{3 \times 4}{2 \times 3} = \frac{12}{6} = 2$

2. You have $23\frac{1}{4}$ L of saline solution. Every student in the class needs $1\frac{1}{2}$ L for an experiment. How many students can do the experiment?

 $23\frac{1}{4} \div 1\frac{1}{2} = \frac{93}{4} \div \frac{3}{2} = \frac{93}{4} \times \frac{2}{3} = \frac{186}{12} = \frac{31}{2} = 15\frac{1}{2};$

 Fifteen students can do the experiment.

3. Because of differences in gravity, your weight on the moon would be $\frac{1}{6}$ what it is on Earth. If you weigh 72 N, what would be your weight on the moon?

 $\frac{1}{6} \times \frac{72}{1} = \frac{72}{6} = 12$; 12 N

Name ______________ Date ________ Class ________

WORKSHEET 16 MATH SKILLS

What Is a Ratio?

Imagine that you are planning a science experiment for your class and you want to make sure you have enough beakers for everyone. What do you do? Well, you could simply count the total number of beakers you have and compare it with the number of students in your class. You may not have realized it, but you just made a ratio! A **ratio** is a comparison between numbers, and can be written in words (3 to 7), as a fraction ($\frac{3}{7}$), or with a colon (3:7).

PROCEDURE: To find the ratio between two quantities, show the two quantities as a fraction, and then reduce. The result is the ratio.

SAMPLE PROBLEM: Find the ratio of thermometers to students if you have 36 thermometers and 48 students in your class.

Step 1: Make the ratio. $\frac{\text{36 thermometers}}{\text{48 students}}$

Step 2: Reduce. $\frac{36}{48} = \frac{36 \div 12}{48 \div 12} = \frac{3}{4}$

The ratio of thermometers to students is 3 to 4, $\frac{3}{4}$, or 3:4.

Wildflower Research Results

Field	Average number of flowers (per 10 m²)	Number of species	Species currently flowering
1	51	12	9
2	17	11	7
3	22	22	20

Analyze Your Data!

1. What is the ratio between the currently flowering species and the total number of species of flowers in Field 1?

 $\frac{9}{12} = \frac{9 \div 3}{12 \div 3} = \frac{3}{4}$, 3 to 4, or 3:4

2. What is the ratio between the number of species currently flowering in Field 1 and Field 2 and the number of species currently flowering in Field 3?

 9 + 7 = 16 species flowering in Field 1 and Field 2; The ratio is $\frac{16}{20} = \frac{16 \div 4}{20 \div 4} = \frac{4}{5}$, 4 to 5, or 4:5.

3. What is the ratio between the number of species currently flowering and the total number of flowers in all three fields?

 9 + 7 + 20 = 36 species currently flowering to 51 + 17 + 22 = 90 flowers;

 $\frac{36}{90} = \frac{36 \div 6}{90 \div 6} = \frac{6}{15} = \frac{6 \div 3}{15 \div 3} = \frac{2}{5}$, 2 to 5, or 2:5

Name ______________ Date ________ Class ________

WORKSHEET 17 MATH SKILLS

Using Proportions and Cross-Multiplication

Ratios are a powerful tool in science and math. But in order to take full advantage of them, we have to do more than just calculate ratios—we have to put them to work! For example, if you have three bacteria specimens for every student in your class, you know that you will have a ratio of 3 to 1, $\frac{3}{1}$, or 3:1. But this ratio does not tell you the total number of specimens. To find that, you need to use a proportion.

A **proportion** is a statement of equality between two ratios. This means that the ratios are equal. It also means that the numerator of one ratio multiplied by the denominator of the other ratio is equal to the product of the other numerator and denominator. An example looks like this:

$$\frac{3}{1} \times \frac{12}{4}$$

$$3 \times 4 = 1 \times 12$$
$$12 = 12$$

Notice that you are multiplying across the equal sign in your proportion. This process is called *cross-multiplication*. Cross-multiplication is useful because if you know three of the quantities in a proportion, you can find the fourth.

PROCEDURE: To find an unknown quantity in a proportion, set up the numbers you know in equal ratios. Leave the place for the quantity you do not know empty for now. Then cross-multiply the known numerator of one ratio with the known denominator of the other. Then divide this product by your remaining known quantity. The quotient is your answer.

SAMPLE PROBLEM: Find the missing number in this proportion:

$$\frac{5}{20} = \frac{?}{100}$$

Step 1: Cross-multiply the known numerator of one ratio with the known denominator of the other ratio.

$$\frac{5}{20} \searrow \frac{?}{100} \rightarrow 5 \times 100 = 500$$

Step 2: Divide this product with your remaining known quantity.

$$500 \div 20 = 25$$

The missing number in the proportion is **25;** $\frac{5}{20} = \frac{25}{100}$

Try It Yourself!

1. Find the unknown quantities in the following proportions:

a. $\frac{3}{8} = \frac{?}{24}$ — $3 \times 24 = 72; 72 \div 8 = 9$

b. $\frac{21}{?} = \frac{63}{21}$ — $21 \times 21 = 441; 441 \div 63 = 7$

c. $\frac{?}{3} = \frac{240}{360}$ — $3 \times 240 = 720; 720 \div 360 = 2$

Name ______________ Date ________ Class ________

2. Are the following ratios equal? Show your work and then write Yes or No.

a. $\frac{2}{4} = \frac{10}{30}$

$2 \times 30 = 60$
$4 \times 10 = 40$
$60 \neq 40$
No

b. $\frac{5}{6} = \frac{15}{2}$

$5 \times 2 = 10$
$6 \times 15 = 90$
$10 \neq 90$
No

c. $\frac{2}{5} = \frac{14}{35}$

$2 \times 35 = 70$
$5 \times 14 = 70$
$70 = 70$
Yes

3. A cookie recipe calls for 2 eggs for every 15 cookies. How many eggs will you need to bake 45 cookies? *Hint:* Set up your proportion like the one in the sample problem, leaving the place for the unknown quantity blank.

$\frac{2}{15} = \frac{?}{45}$; $2 \times 45 = 90; 90 \div 15 = 6$; You will need 6 eggs.

4. The ratio of turtles to fish in a pond is 2 to 5.

a. If the pond has 20 fish, how many turtles are there?

$\frac{2}{5} = \frac{?}{20}$; $2 \times 20 = 40; 40 \div 5 = 8$; There are 8 turtles.

b. How many fish are there if the pond contains 6 turtles?

$\frac{2}{5} = \frac{6}{?}$; $5 \times 6 = 30; 30 \div 2 = 15$; There are 15 fish.

Challenge Yourself!

5. In a bird sanctuary, 2 out of every 12 birds are eagles, the ratio of hawks to eagles is 1 to 1, the ratio of woodpeckers to hawks is 1 to 2, and the ratio of hawks to cardinals is 1 to 2.

a. The bird sanctuary also has sparrows. How many birds out of every 12 are sparrows?

2 eagles + 2 hawks + 1 woodpecker + 4 cardinals = 9 birds; $12 - 9 = 3$; There are 3 sparrows for every 12 birds.

b. How many cardinals are there for every 180 birds?

$\frac{\text{cardinals}}{\text{birds}} = \frac{4}{12} = \frac{1}{3}$; $\frac{1}{3} = \frac{?}{180}$; $1 \times 180 = 180; 180 \div 3 = 60$; There are 60 cardinals for every 180 birds.

MATH SKILLS

Name ______________ Date ________ Class ________

WORKSHEET

18 MATH SKILLS

Decimals and Fractions

Many numbers you will use in science class and other places will be decimal numbers. Like fractions, **decimals** are used to show *how much,* or *what part,* of a whole. A decimal point (.) separates the whole number part of a decimal number on the left from the fraction part on the right. The value of a decimal number is determined by its *place value.* The chart on the right shows the place values for the decimal system. The first place after the decimal point shows parts of ten, or tenths, the second place shows hundredths, and so on. For example, 3.74 is the same as $3 + \frac{7}{10} + \frac{4}{100}$. Any fraction can be changed into a decimal number, and vice versa.

tens	ones	tenths	hundredths	thousandths	ten thousandths
0	0.	0	0	0	0

PROCEDURE: *To change a fraction into a decimal,* divide the numerator of the fraction by the denominator. If you have a mixed number (a whole number with a fraction), put the whole-number part of your number before the decimal point.

SAMPLE PROBLEM A: Change $24\frac{3}{20}$ into a decimal number.

Step 1: Divide the numerator of the fraction by the denominator. Notice that 20 does not divide evenly into 3. Therefore, you will need to add zeros after a decimal point in the numerator so that you can divide into it. The answer will be a decimal to show what part of 20 will divide into 3.

$$\begin{array}{r} 0.15 \\ 20\overline{)3.00} \\ -20 \\ \hline 100 \\ -100 \\ \hline 0 \end{array}$$

Step 2: Because $24\frac{3}{20}$ is a mixed number, put the whole number before the decimal point.

$$24\frac{3}{20} = 24.15$$

PROCEDURE: *To change a decimal into a fraction,* put the decimal over its place value and reduce.

SAMPLE PROBLEM B: Convert 0.25 into a fraction. Because 0.25 is in the *hundredths* place, put 25 over 100 and reduce.

$$\frac{25}{100} = \frac{1}{4}$$

1. Change the fractions and mixed numbers into decimal numbers.

a. $\frac{5}{10} =$ $5 \div 10 = 0.5$

b. $7\frac{66}{100} =$ $\frac{66}{100}$; 0.66; $7\frac{66}{100} = 7.66$

c. $\frac{15}{25} =$ $15 \div 25 = 0.6$

d. $\frac{165}{55} =$ $165 \div 55 = 3$

2. Convert each decimal number to a fraction or a mixed number.

a. $0.13 =$ $\frac{13}{100}$

b. $8.405 =$ $8\frac{405}{1000} = 8\frac{81}{200}$

c. $2.98 =$ $2\frac{98}{100} = 2\frac{49}{50}$

d. $0.0001 =$ $\frac{1}{10,000}$

Name ______________ Date ________ Class ________

WORKSHEET

19 MATH SKILLS

Arithmetic with Decimals

How much would you expect to pay if you were buying a bag of chips for 50 cents and a cola for 75 cents? $1.25, right? Well, if you knew that one, you already know how to add decimals. Doing arithmetic with decimals is a lot like doing arithmetic with whole numbers. Read on to see how it's done.

Part 1: Adding and Subtracting Decimals

PROCEDURE: To add or subtract decimals, line up your numbers vertically so that the decimal points line up. Then add or subtract the columns from right to left, carrying or borrowing numbers when necessary.

SAMPLE PROBLEM: Add the following numbers: 3.1415 and 2.96.

Step1: Line up the numbers vertically so that the decimal points line up.

$$\begin{array}{r} 3.1415 \\ +2.96 \\ \hline \end{array}$$

Step 2: Add the columns from right to left, carrying when necessary.

$$\begin{array}{r} {\scriptstyle 1\,1} \\ 3.1415 \\ +2.96 \\ \hline 6.1015 \end{array}$$

The sum is **6.1015.**

Do Some Decimal Math!

1. Match the expressions on the left with the letter for their correct answer on the right.

a. 3.2 + 1.9 C — **A.** 55.11

b. 8.91 − 0.891 D — **B.** 0.809

c. 50.1 + 5.01 A — **C.** 5.1

d. 0.999 − 0.19 B — **D.** 8.019

2. The distance indicator, or odometer, on Robyn's family car reads 32795.2 after a summer vacation. The family drove 631.4 km on the trip. What did the odometer read before the trip?

32795.2 − 631.4 = 32163.8

3. Sloane has $12 to spend at the hobby shop. Does he have enough money to buy a 5 m rope for $5.64, a bucket of paint for $3.75, and a pack of construction paper for $2.39?

5.64 + 3.75 + 2.39 = 11.78; Yes, Sloane has enough money.

Name ______________ Date ________ Class ________

Arithmetic with Decimals, continued

Part 2: Multiplying Decimal Numbers

PROCEDURE: To multiply decimal numbers, align the numbers vertically and put the number with the most digits on top. Multiply the top number by the bottom number, just like you would multiply whole numbers. Then count the total number of decimal places in both of the multipliers. In your product, move the decimal point to the left the same number of places as there are in the multipliers.

SAMPLE PROBLEM: What is 1.12 × 2.3?

Step 1: Align the numbers vertically, with the longer number on top, and multiply.	**Step 2:** Count the total number of decimal places in both numbers being multiplied.	**Step 3:** Because there is a total of 3 decimal places in your numbers, move the decimal point in your product 3 places to the *left*.
1.12 × 2.3 336 2240 2576	1.12 × 2.3 There is a total of **3** decimal places.	2,5,7,6 → 2.576

The product of 1.12 and 2.3 is **2.576.**

Produce Some Products!

4. Calculate the products. Remember to show all your work. If you need more space, use your ScienceLog or a separate sheet of paper.

a. 0.73 × 0.5 = 0.365

b. 5.23 × 1.9
4707
523
9.937

c. 9.12 × 8 = 72.96

d. 1.12 × 0.21
112
224
0.2352

e. 90.5 × 0.73
2715
6335
66.065

f. 0.125 × 0.3 = 0.0375

5. A typical amoeba is 0.0008 m long. Placed end to end, how long would 150 amoebas be?

0.0008 × 150 = 0.12; 0.12 m

Challenge Yourself!

6. A hockey player has a career average of 0.9 goals per game during the regular season and 1.6 goals per game in the playoffs. How many goals would you expect him to score in 81 regular season games and 16 playoff games?

81 × 0.9 = 72.9; 16 × 1.6 = 25.6; 72.9 + 25.6 = 98.5; 98.5 goals

Name ______________ Date ________ Class ________

Arithmetic with Decimals, continued

Part 3: Dividing Decimal Numbers

PROCEDURE: To divide decimal numbers, move the decimal point in the divisor to the right until it is a whole number. Then move the decimal point in the dividend to the right the same number of places. Place a decimal point in the quotient directly above the decimal point in the dividend. Finally, divide as with whole numbers.

SAMPLE PROBLEM: 2.5)8.625

Step 1: Move the decimal point in the divisor to the right until it is a whole number.	**Step 2:** Move the decimal point in the dividend to the right the same number of places, and place a decimal point above it in the quotient.
2,5,)8.625	25)8,6,25

Step 3: Divide as with whole numbers.

```
    3.45
25)86.25
  -75
   112
  -100
    125
   -125
      0
```

2.5)8.625 = **3.45**

Decimal Division

7. Find the quotients for the following division problems, showing all of your work. If you need more space, use your ScienceLog or a separate piece of paper.

a. 0.2)4.6 = 23

b. 0.03)99.6 = 3320

c. 7)36.4 = 5.2

d. 0.5)95.5 = 191

e. 6)240.18 = 40.03

f. 0.4)6.24 = 15.6

8. The snowfall in a year in Peanut Valley was 74.76 cm. What was the average monthly snowfall?

74.76 ÷ 12 = 6.23; 6.23 cm

9. After constructing a fence around your yard, you calculate that you used 234.5 m of fencing materials. Your yard has a perimeter of 26.8 m. How much fencing material did you use per meter of your yard?

234.5 ÷ 26.8 = 8.75; 8.75 m

Name ______________________ Date ____________ Class ____________

WORKSHEET
20 MATH SKILLS

Parts of 100: Calculating Percentages

Let's say you scored 85 percent (%) on your last science test. Does that mean you got 85 questions right? Probably not. The score on your test is expressed as a percentage. The word *percent* comes from Latin words meaning "parts of a 100," and that's exactly what a percentage is. A **percentage** is a ratio that compares a number with 100. Read on to learn how to find a percentage of a number.

PROCEDURE: To find a percentage of a number, first rewrite the percentage you wish to find as a decimal by moving its decimal point two places to the *left*. Then multiply this decimal number by the number you are finding the percentage of. The result is your percentage.

SAMPLE PROBLEM: What is 85% of 40?

Step 1: Rewrite the percentage by moving the decimal point two places to the left.

85% → 8 5 → 0.85

Step 2: Multiply the decimal by the number you are calculating the percentage of.

0.85 × 40 = 34
85% of 40 is **34.**

Practice Your Percentages!

1. Calculate the percentages of the following numbers:

a. 30% of 100 0.30 × 100 = 30

b. 90% of 45 0.90 × 45 = 40.5

c. 67% of 67 0.67 × 67 = 44.89

d. 4% of 25 0.04 × 25 = 1

e. 15% of 225 0.15 × 225 = 33.75

f. 3.5% of 40 0.035 × 40 = 1.400 = 1.4

2. You read in the local paper that the eagle population in Holler State Park has increased 25 percent since 1994. If the population of eagles in 1994 was 28 eagles, how many live in the park now?

28 × 0.25 = 7; 28 + 7 = 35 eagles

Challenge Yourself!

3. During a summer drought, a city's water supply is decreased by 35 percent. If the city had a reserve of 45 million liters of water before the drought, how much do they have today?

45,000,000 L × 0.35 = 15,750,000 L;

45,000,000 L − 15,750,000 L = 29,250,000 L

Name ______________________ Date ____________ Class ____________

WORKSHEET
21 MATH SKILLS

Percentages, Fractions, and Decimals

Imagine that your science class is doing a school survey to determine which eye colors are most common. The report from the sixth-grade class says that $\frac{3}{5}$ of the students have black or brown eyes, while $\frac{2}{5}$ have blue or green eyes. The seventh-grade class reports that 45 percent have black or brown eyes, and 55 percent have blue or green eyes. The eighth-grade class reports that 0.8 have black or brown eyes, and 0.2 have blue or green eyes. Yikes! Each class has a different way of showing its data! So how do you compare the reports? Well, it's not as complicated as it might look. You see, percentages, fractions, and decimals are just different ways of expressing the same information. Each one tells you *how much* or *how many* of a certain amount. As you learned on the last page, a percentage can be changed to a decimal. For example, 45 percent is equal to 0.45. Percentages can also be changed into fractions. Likewise, every fraction can be expressed as a decimal or percentage, and so on. When comparing numbers or doing operations with numbers, it is often easier to have all of your numbers in the same form before doing calculations.

PROCEDURE 1: To change a fraction to a decimal or percentage, divide the numerator of the fraction by the denominator to make a decimal. To change the decimal number into a percentage, move the decimal point two places to the *right.*

SAMPLE PROBLEM: Change $\frac{3}{5}$ into a decimal number and a percentage.

Step 1: Divide the numerator by the denominator.

3 ÷ 5 = 0.6

Step 2: To change the decimal into a percentage, move the decimal point two places to the right.

0.6 → 0 6 0 → **60%**

PROCEDURE 2: To change a decimal number into a fraction or percentage, place the decimal over its place value and reduce. To change a decimal into a percentage, see Step 2 of Procedure 1.

SAMPLE PROBLEM: Express 0.56 as a fraction and a percentage.

Step 1: Because 0.56 is in the *hundredths* place, put the whole number over 100 and reduce.

$\frac{56}{100} = \frac{14}{25}$

Step 2: To change a decimal into a percentage, move the decimal point two places to the right, as in step 2 of procedure 1.

0.56 → 0 5 6 → 56%

Practice What You've Learned

1. Express the following percentages as decimal numbers:

a. 52% 5 2 → 0.52

b. 99% 9 9 → 0.99

c. 7.8% 0 7 8 → 0.078

d. 0.57% 0 0 57 → 0.0057

Name ______________ Date ________ Class ________

2. Express the following fractions as both a decimal number and a percentage.

a. $\frac{75}{100}$ = $75 \div 100 = 0.75$; 75% **b.** $\frac{1}{8}$ = $1 \div 8 = 0.125$; 12.5%

c. $\frac{9}{20}$ = $9 \div 20 = 0.45$; 45% **d.** $\frac{12}{4}$ = $12 \div 4 = 3$; 300%

e. $\frac{26}{13}$ = $26 \div 13 = 2$; 200% **f.** $\frac{8}{32}$ = $8 \div 32 = 0.25$; 25%

3. Change the following decimal numbers into both a fraction and a percentage:

a. 0.3 = $\frac{3}{10}$; 30% **b.** 0.12 = $\frac{12}{100}$; 12%

c. 0.99 = $\frac{99}{100}$; 99% **d.** 1.5 = $\frac{3}{2}$; 150%

e. 0.505 = $\frac{505}{1000}$; 50.5% **f.** 0.01 = $\frac{1}{100}$; 1%

4. Write True or False next to each equation.

a. $2\frac{2}{5} = 2.4 = 24\%$ False

b. $0.03 = 3\% = \frac{3}{100}$ True

c. $0.45\% = \frac{90}{200} = 0.0045$ False

d. $5.25 = 5\frac{14}{28} = 525\%$ False

5. Convert the following equations into the same form and calculate. Hint: Do the calculation inside the parentheses before adding or subtracting.

a. $\frac{2}{5} + 0.12 =$ $\frac{2}{5} + \frac{12}{100} = \frac{52}{100} = \frac{13}{25}$

b. $(75\% \text{ of } 60) - 3\frac{3}{5} =$ $\frac{45}{1} - 3\frac{3}{5} = 41\frac{2}{5}$

c. $\frac{32}{8} - (15\% \text{ of } 20) =$ $\frac{32}{8} - \frac{3}{1} = 1$

Name ______________ Date ________ Class ________

WORKSHEET 22 MATH SKILLS

Working with Percentages and Proportions

When working with percentages, it is often helpful to think of them in terms of ratios and proportions. For instance, if someone asks you, "What is 10% of 40?" you could simply change 10% into a decimal (0.1) and multiply it by 40 to get 4. But what if you were asked, "5% of what number is 10?" That's a little trickier. To do this calculation, it is convenient to use a proportion.

PROCEDURE: To use percentages in a proportion, first put your known percentage in a ratio with 100. Then create an equivalent ratio, leaving the place for your unknown quantity blank. Cross-multiply the known numerator with the known denominator. Divide the product with your remaining known value. The result is your unknown quantity.

SAMPLE PROBLEM: 25% of what number is 4?

Step 1: Put your percentage in a ratio with 100. $\frac{25}{100}$	**Step 2:** Create an equivalent ratio, leaving the space for the unknown quantity blank. $\frac{25}{100} = \frac{4}{?}$
Step 3: Cross-multiply the known numerator with the known denominator. $\frac{25}{100} \nearrow \frac{4}{?} \rightarrow 100 \times 4 = 400$	**Step 4:** Divide the product with the remaining known quantity. $400 \div 25 = 16$

25% of **16** is 4.

Figure It Out!

1. Follow the steps above to answer the following questions:

a. 15% of what number is 3? $\frac{15}{100} = \frac{3}{?}$; $3 \times 100 = 300$; $300 \div 15 = 20$

b. 25% of what number is 11? $\frac{25}{100} = \frac{11}{?}$; $11 \times 100 = 1100$; $1100 \div 25 = 44$

c. 8% of what number is 4? $\frac{8}{100} = \frac{4}{?}$; $4 \times 100 = 400$; $400 \div 8 = 50$

d. 24% of what number is 168? $\frac{24}{100} = \frac{168}{?}$; $168 \times 100 = 16{,}800$; $16{,}800 \div 24 = 700$

2. A biologist estimates that the number of frogs living in Lasso Pond increased last summer by about 70 frogs. If this represents a 25 percent increase, how many frogs lived in the pond before last summer?

$\frac{25}{100} = \frac{70}{?}$; $70 \times 100 = 7000$; $7000 \div 25 = 280$; 280 frogs lived in the pond before last summer.

Name ______ Date ______ Class ______

WORKSHEET 23 MATH SKILLS

Counting the Zeros

A **power of 10** is a number that can have 10 as its only factors. For instance, $(10 \times 10) = 100$ and $(10 \times 10 \times 10 \times 10) = 10{,}000$ are both powers of 10. Multiplying and dividing by powers of 10 is as easy as counting the zeros and moving your decimal point the same number of places.

Part 1: Multiplying by Powers of 10

PROCEDURE: To multiply a number by a power of 10, move the decimal point to the *right* the same number of places as there are zeros in the power of 10. If there are not enough places in your number to do this, you will need to add zeros to the number as place holders.

SAMPLE PROBLEM: Multiply 8.25 by 10, 100, and 1000.

10 × 8.25 = 8.2 5 → 82.5
100 × 8.25 = 8.2 5 → 825
1000 × 8.25 = 8.2 5 0 → 8250

It's Your Turn!

1. Write your answers on the lines, and remember to place commas in the appropriate places.

a. 10 × 6 = 6 0 → 60
b. 9.381 × 100 = 9 3 8 1 → 938.1
c. 71 × 100 = 71 0 0 → 7100
d. 1000 × 41 = 41 0 0 0 → 41,000
e. 10 × 11.9 = 11 9 → 119
f. 67 × 10,000 = 67 0 0 0 0 → 670,000

Part 2: Dividing by Powers of 10

PROCEDURE: To divide a number by a power of 10, move the decimal point to the left as many places as there are zeros in the power of 10.

SAMPLE PROBLEM: Divide 763 by 10, 1000, and 100,000.

763 ÷ **10** = 76 3 → 76.3
763 ÷ **1000** = 7 6 3 → 0.763
763 ÷ **100,000** = 0 0 7 6 3 → 0.00763

2. Divide by powers of 10.

a. 55 ÷ 1000 = 0 5 5 → 0.055
b. 9907 ÷ 100 = 99 0 7 → 99.07
c. 620 ÷ 10 = 62 0 → 62
d. 4.01 ÷ 100 = 0 4.01 → 0.0401
e. 0.04 ÷ 1000 = 0 0 0 04 → 0.00004
f. 996 ÷ 10,000 = 0 9 9 6 → 0.0996

Name ______ Date ______ Class ______

WORKSHEET 24 MATH SKILLS

Creating Exponents

Imagine that you are writing a paper for your science class and need to write many very large numbers, such as 10,000,000,000,000. Your fingers would get pretty tired writing all those zeros. However, there is a simpler way to express these large powers of 10. An **exponent** is a small number placed above and to the right of a base number to show how many times the base number is multiplied by itself. For example, 100,000 is 10 multiplied by itself five times, or $10 \times 10 \times 10 \times 10 \times 10$. Written in exponential form, 100,000 is 10^5. The exponent number tells you how many zeros are in your power of 10.

PROCEDURE: To change a power of 10 into exponential form, first count the number of zeros in your power of 10. This number will be your exponent. Place the exponent above and to the right of the base number of 10.

SAMPLE PROBLEM: Write 10,000,000,000,000 in exponential form.

Step 1: Count the zeros in your power of 10.	**Step 2:** Place your exponent above and to the right of your base number 10.
10,000,000,000,000 has 13 zeros.	10^{13}

10,000,000,000,000 = $\mathbf{10^{13}}$

On Your Own!

1. Convert the following powers of 10 into exponential form:

a. 1000 = 10^3
b. 10,000,000 = 10^7
c. 1,000,000 = 10^6
d. 10,000,000,000 = 10^{10}
e. 10,000,000,000,000,000,000,000,000,000,000,000 = 10^{34}

2. Change the following exponent numbers into powers of 10:

a. 10^5 = 100,000
b. 10^2 = 100
c. 10^9 = 1,000,000,000
d. 10^{12} = 1,000,000,000,000
e. 10^{29} = 100,000,000,000,000,000,000,000,000,000

ANSWER KEY

Name ______________________ Date __________ Class __________

WORKSHEET

25 MATH SKILLS

What Is Scientific Notation?

Sometimes scientific calculations result in very large numbers, like 918,700,000,000,000, or in very small numbers, such as 0.0000000578. **Scientific notation** is a short way of representing such numbers without writing the place-holding zeros. In scientific notation, we write the number as a product of two factors: the first is a number between 1 and 10, and the second is a power of ten, written as $10^{exponent}$.

PROCEDURE: To write a number in scientific notation, first identify which digits are not place-holding zeros. Then place the decimal point after the leftmost digit. To find the exponent for the factor of 10, count the number of places that you moved the decimal point. If you moved the decimal point to the left, the exponent will be positive. If you moved the decimal point to the right, the exponent will be negative.

SAMPLE PROBLEM: Write 653,000,000 in scientific notation.

Step 1: Identify the number without the place-holding zeros.

653

Step 2: Place the decimal point after the leftmost digit.

6.53

Step 3: Find the exponent by counting the number of places that you moved the decimal point.

6,5,3,0,0,0,0,0,0 → 6.53

The decimal point was moved 8 places to the left. Therefore, the exponent of 10 is positive 8. *Remember*, if the decimal point had moved to the right, the exponent would be negative.

Step 4: Write the number in scientific notation.

$\mathbf{6.53 \times 10^8}$

Practice Your Skills!

Original number	Number without place-holding zeros	Power of 10	Number in scientific notation
1. 530,000	5.3	10^5	5.3×10^5
2. 904,580,000	9.0458	10^8	9.0458×10^8
3. 0.000000617	6.17	10^{-7}	6.17×10^{-7}

4. Express the following data in scientific notation:

a. 53,657 kg 5.3657×10^4 kg **b.** 0.000043 L 4.3×10^{-5} L

c. 0.00083 m 8.3×10^{-4} m **d.** 1011.9 cm 1.0119×10^3 cm

Name ______________________ Date __________ Class __________

WORKSHEET

26 MATH SKILLS

Multiplying and Dividing in Scientific Notation

Part 1: Multiplying in Scientific Notation

PROCEDURE: To multiply numbers in scientific notation, multiply the decimal numbers. Then *add* the exponents of the powers of 10. Place the new power of 10 with the decimal in scientific notation form. If your decimal number is greater than 10, count the number of times the decimal moves to the left, and add this number to the exponent.

SAMPLE PROBLEM: Multiply (2.6×10^7) by (6.3×10^4).

Step 1: Multiply the decimal numbers.

$2.6 \times 6.3 = 16.38$

Step 2: Add the exponents.

$7 + 4 = 11$

Step 3: Put the new decimal number with the new exponent in scientific notation form.

16.38×10^{11}

Step 4: Because the new decimal number is greater than 10, count the number of places the decimal moves to put the number between 1 and 10. Add this number to the exponent. In this case, the decimal point moves one place, so add 1 to the exponent.

$16.38 \times 10^{11} \rightarrow 1.638 \times 10^{12}$

Try It Yourself!

1. Follow the steps in the Sample Problem carefully to complete the following equations.

Multiplying with Scientific Notations

Problem	New decimal	New exponent	Answer
Sample problem: $(4.4 \times 10^6) \times (3.9 \times 10^4)$	$4.4 \times 3.9 = 17.16$	$6 + 4 = 10$	1.716×10^{11}
a. $(2.8 \times 10^8) \times (1.9 \times 10^4)$	5.32	12	5.32×10^{12}
b. $(1.3 \times 10^9) \times (4.7 \times 10^{-5})$	6.11	4	6.11×10^4
c. $(3.7 \times 10^{15}) \times (5.2 \times 10^7)$	19.24	22	1.924×10^{23}
d. $(4.9 \times 10^{24}) \times (1.6 \times 10^5)$	7.84	29	7.84×10^{29}

2. The mass of one hydrogen atom is 1.67×10^{-27} kg. A cylinder contains 3.01×10^{23} hydrogen atoms. What is the mass of the hydrogen?

$1.67 \times 3.01 = 5.0267$; $23 + (-27) = -4$; 5.0267×10^{-4} kg

Name ______ Date ______ Class ______

Part 2: Dividing in Scientific Notation

PROCEDURE: To divide numbers in scientific notation, first divide the decimal numbers. Then *subtract* the exponents of your power of 10. Place the new power of 10 with the decimal in scientific notation form. If the resulting decimal number is less than 1, move the decimal point to the right and decrease the exponent by the number of places that the decimal point moved.

SAMPLE PROBLEM: Divide (1.23×10^{11}) by (2.4×10^{4}).

Step 1: Divide the decimal numbers.	**Step 2:** Subtract the exponents of the powers of 10.
$1.23 \div 2.4 = 0.5125$	$11 - 4 = 7$
Step 3: Place the new power of 10 with the new decimal in scientific notation form.	**Step 4:** Because the decimal number is not between 1 and 10, move the decimal point one place to the right and decrease the exponent by 1.
0.5125×10^{7}	$0.5125 \times 10^{7} \rightarrow 5.125 \times 10^{6}$

$(1.23 \times 10^{11}) \div (2.4 \times 10^{4}) = \mathbf{5.125 \times 10^{6}}$

3. Complete the following chart:

Dividing with Scientific Notation

Problem	New decimal	New exponent	Answer
Sample problem: $(5.76 \times 10^{9}) \div (3.2 \div 10^{3})$	$5.76 \div 3.2 = 1.8$	$9 - 3 = 6$	1.8×10^{6}
a. $(3.72 \times 10^{8}) \div (1.2 \times 10^{5})$	3.1	3	3.1×10^{3}
b. $(6.4 \times 10^{-4}) \div (4 \times 10^{6})$	1.6	−10	1.6×10^{-10}
c. $(3.6 \times 10^{4}) \div (6 \times 10^{5})$	0.6	−1	6×10^{-2}
d. $(1.44 \times 10^{24}) \div (1.2 \times 10^{17})$	1.2	7	1.2×10^{7}

4. The average distance from Earth to the sun is 1.5×10^{11} m. The speed of light is 3×10^{8} m/s. Approximately how long does it take for light to travel from the sun to Earth?

$1.5 \div 3 = 0.5$; $11 - 8 = 3$; 0.5×10^{3} seconds $= 5 \times 10^{2}$ seconds

Name ______ Date ______ Class ______

Work with the System!

1. Write True or False next to each statement.

a. 12 hg = 1.2 kg True **b.** 54 cm = 5.4 mm False

c. 0.5 dL = 0.005 cL False **d.** 4.5 g = 0.45 dag True

e. 111 cm = 1.11 m True **f.** 7 cL = 70,000 kL False

2. Fill in the missing numbers and units in the equations below.

a. 25 mm = 2.5 cm **b.** 27 kg = 270,000 dg

c. 50 cm = 0.005 hm **d.** 1.2 dL = 0.12 L

e. 0.9 L= 900 mL **f.** 41 hm = 4,100,000 mm

3. 1 m = 10 dm = 100 cm = 1000 mm

4. 5 kg = 50 hg = 50,000 dg = 500,000 cg

5. Special balances can weigh to the 0.00000001 g. How many kilograms is this?

0.00000001 g = 0.00000000001 kg

6. A chemistry experiment calls for 5 g of baking soda. Your measuring spoon holds 5000 mg of powder. How many scoops will you need for the experiment?

5 g = 5000 mg; You will need 1 scoop.

Challenge Yourself!

Some SI prefixes are almost never used because they are so small or large. A micrometer (µm) is 10^{-6} m, while a nanometer is 10^{-9} m. A gigameter is 10^{9} m.

7. a. How many nanometers are in 1 gigameter?

1 gigameter = 1,000,000,000,000,000,000 nanometers

b. How many gigameters are in 1,000,000,000,000 micrometers?

1,000,000,000,000 micrometers = 0.001 gigameters

ANSWER KEY

Name ______________________ Date __________ Class __________

WORKSHEET 28 MATH SKILLS

A Formula for SI Catch-up

Scientists use SI all the time. But most people in the United States still use non-SI units. So what do you do if you have data in non-SI units and you want to convert the data into SI units, or vice versa? Have no fear! Conversion charts, like the one shown below, can help you accomplish the task with ease.

SI Conversion Chart

If you know	Multiply by	To find
inches (in.)	2.54	centimeters (cm)
feet (ft)	30.50	centimeters (cm)
yards (yd)	0.91	meters (m)
miles (mi)	1.61	kilometers (km)
ounces (oz)	28.35	grams (g)
pounds (lb)	0.45	kilograms (kg)
fluid ounces (fl oz)	29.57	milliliters (mL)
cups (c)	0.24	liters (L)
pints (pt)	0.47	liters (L)
quarts (qt)	0.94	liters (L)
gallons (gal)	3.79	liters (L)

PROCEDURE: *To convert from non-SI units to SI units,* find the non-SI unit in the left column and multiply it by the number in the center column. The resulting number will be in the SI unit in the right column.

To convert a SI unit into a non-SI unit, find the SI unit in the right column and divide by the number in the center column to get the non-SI unit on the left.

SAMPLE PROBLEM: Convert 15 gal into liters (L).

$15 \times 3.79 = \mathbf{56.85\ L}$

Complete the Conversions!

1. Use the SI conversion chart to do the following conversions (round to the nearest hundredths):

a. 15 oz = (15 × 28.35) = 425.25 g **b.** 40 cm = (40 ÷ 2.54) = 15.75 in.

c. 2 c = (2 × 0.24) = 0.48 L **d.** 27 m = (27 ÷ 0.91) = 29.67 yd

e. 5.5 gal = (5.5 × 3.79) = 20.85 L **f.** 115 lb = (115 × 0.45) = 51.75 kg

MATH SKILLS

Name ______________________ Date __________ Class __________

A Formula for SI Catch-up, continued

2. A chemistry experiment calls for 6 mL of HCl (hydrochloric acid). How many fluid ounces is this?

6 mL ÷ 29.57 fl oz/mL = 0.2 fl oz

3. Simone wants to compete in a 15 km run. The farthest she can run is 10 mi. Can she finish the race?

10 mi × 1.61 km/mi = 16.1 km; Yes, she can finish the race.

4. A cake recipe calls for 1 cup of milk. How many milliliters is this?

1 c × 0.24 L/c = 0.24 L; 0.24 L = 240 mL

5. Julie is 162 cm tall. How tall is she in feet?

162 cm ÷ 30.5 cm/ft = 5.31 ft

6. George ran 1000 yd in gym class. How many kilometers did he run?

1000 yd × 0.91 m/yd = 900 m; 900 m ÷ 1000 km/m = 0.9 km

7. Alejandro weighed 8 lb, 4 oz when he was born. How many grams did he weigh?

8 lb × 0.45 kg/lb = 3.6 kg; 3.6 kg × 1000 g/kg = 3600 g; 4 oz × 28.35 g/oz = 113.4 g;

3600 g + 113.4 g = 3713.4 g. He weighed 3713.4 g.

Name ______________ Date ________ Class ________

WORKSHEET 29 **MATH SKILLS**

Finding Perimeter and Area

Suppose your class has been asked to build a garden for your school. In order to keep the garden clean and undisturbed, your class decides to build a fence around the outside of it. How much fencing material will you need? The answer to this question can be found with geometry. The distance around the outside of any figure is called the **perimeter** *(P)*. In the case of the garden, the perimeter will equal the total length of the fence.

Part 1: Calculating Perimeter

PROCEDURE: To find the perimeter of a figure, add the lengths of all the sides.

SAMPLE PROBLEM: Find the perimeter *(P)* of the figure.

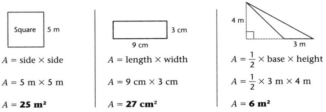

$9 + 5 + 4 + 7 + 10 + 4 + 5 + 8 = 52$

$P =$ **52 m**

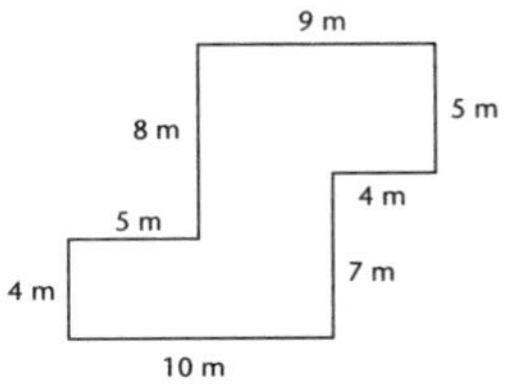

1. Using a metric ruler, measure the sides of the figures below in centimeters, and calculate the perimeter of each figure.

a.

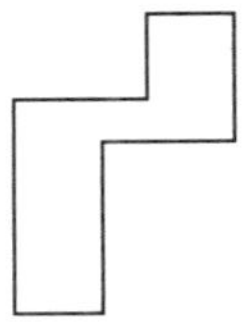

$P =$ 12 cm

b.

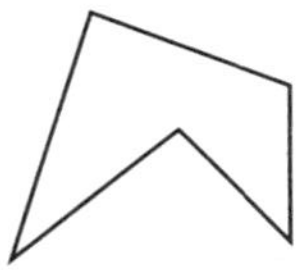

$P =$ 11.3 cm

c.

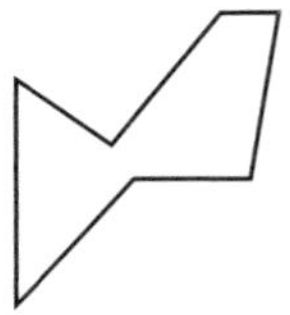

$P =$ 11.7 cm

2. Use the lengths to determine the perimeter of the figures.

a. Rectangle: length = 4m, width = 2m

$P =$ 12 m

b. Square: side = 45 mm

$P =$ $45 \times 4 = 180$ mm

c. Equilateral triangle: side = 6 m

$P =$ $6 \times 3 = 18$ m

d. Rectangle: length = 3.5 cm, width = 2.4 cm

$P =$ 11.8 cm

MATH SKILLS

Name ______________ Date ________ Class ________

Part 2: Calculating Area

Now that you know how to find the perimeter of the garden, you are ready to plan what to grow. How much planting soil will you need? How many plants will fit in the garden? To answer these questions, you will need to know the area of the garden. **Area** *(A)* is the number of square units needed to cover the surface of a figure. The equations below will help you find the area of some common figures.

EQUATIONS: Area of a square = side × side

Area of a rectangle = length × width

Area of a triangle = $\frac{1}{2}$ × base × height

SAMPLE PROBLEMS: Find the area *(A)* of each of the following figures:

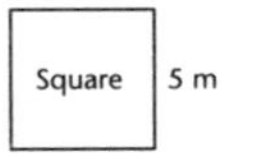

A = side × side

$A = 5\text{ m} \times 5\text{ m}$

$A =$ **25 m²**

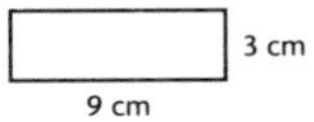

A = length × width

$A = 9\text{ cm} \times 3\text{ cm}$

$A =$ **27 cm²**

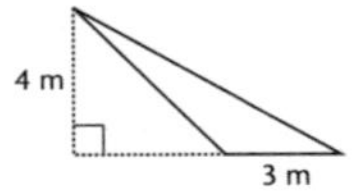

$A = \frac{1}{2} \times \text{base} \times \text{height}$

$A = \frac{1}{2} \times 3\text{ m} \times 4\text{ m}$

$A =$ **6 m²**

Area Alert!

3. Find the area of each figure below. *Hint:* When finding the area of irregular figures, first divide the figures up into triangles, squares, and rectangles and then add their individual areas.

a.

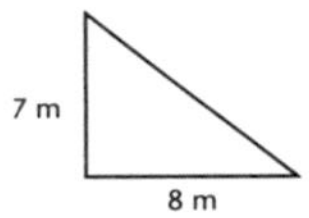

$A = \frac{1}{2} \times 7\text{ m} \times 8\text{ m} = 28\text{ m}^2$

b.

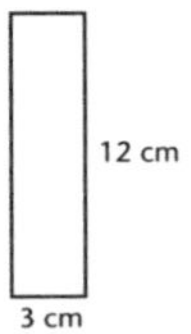

$A = 12\text{ cm} \times 3\text{ cm} = 36\text{ cm}^2$

c.

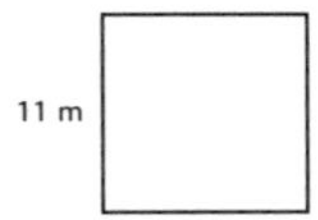

$A = 11\text{ m} \times 11\text{ m} = 121\text{ m}^2$

d.

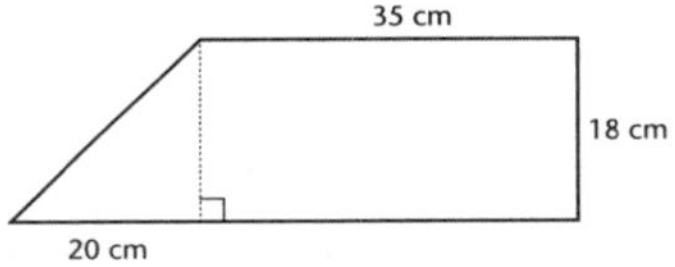

$A = 180\text{ cm}^2 + 630\text{ cm}^2 = 810\text{ cm}^2$

e.

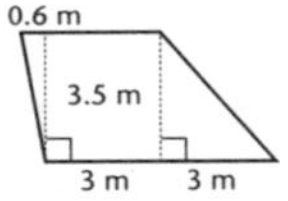

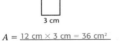

$A = 1.05\text{ m}^2 + 10.5\text{ m}^2 + 5.25\text{ m}^2 = 16.8\text{ m}^2$

Name ______________ Date ________ Class ________

WORKSHEET 30 MATH SKILLS

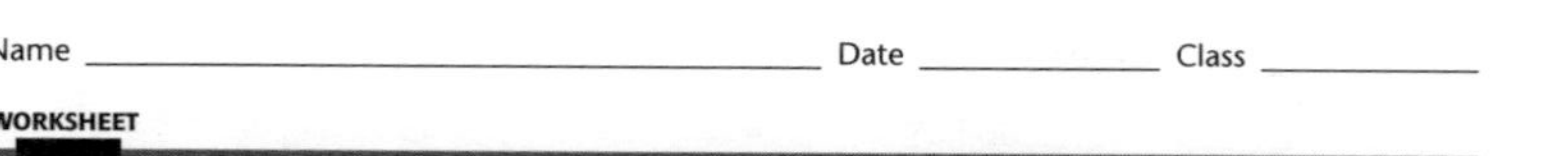

Finding Volume

Volume (V) is the amount of space something occupies. It is expressed in cubic units, such as cubic meters (m^3) and cubic centimeters (cm^3). Use the equations for volume below to calculate the volume of cubes and prisms.

EQUATIONS: Volume of a cube = side × side × side
Volume of a prism = area of base × height

SAMPLE PROBLEMS: Find the volume (V) of the solids.

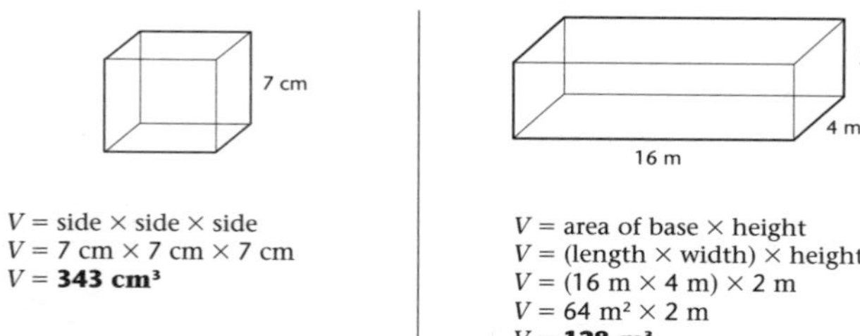

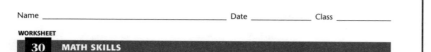

V = side × side × side
V = 7 cm × 7 cm × 7 cm
V = **343 cm³**

V = area of base × height
V = (length × width) × height
V = (16 m × 4 m) × 2 m
V = 64 m² × 2 m
V = **128 m³**

Turn Up the Volume!

1. Find the volume of the solids.

a.

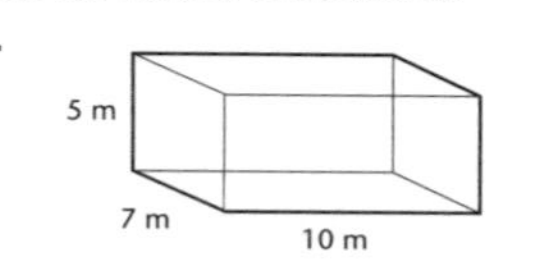

V = 10 m × 7 m × 5 m = 350 m³

b.

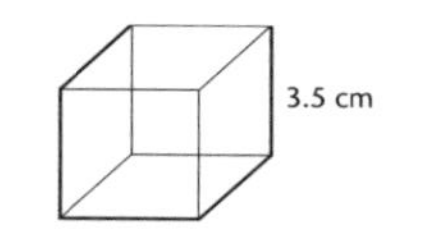

V = 3.5 cm × 3.5 cm × 3.5 cm = 42.875 cm³

c. 3 cm, 0.25 cm, 0.5 cm

V = 0.25 cm × 0.5 cm × 3 cm = 0.375 cm³

d. 8 cm, 6 cm, 300 cm

V = 8 cm × 6 cm × 300 cm = 14,400 cm³

Challenge Yourself!

2. A rectangular-shaped swimming pool is 50 m long and 2.5 m deep and holds 2500 m³ of water. What is the width of the pool?

50 m × 2.5 m = 125 m²; 2500 m³ ÷ 125 m² = 20 m

Name ______________ Date ________ Class ________

WORKSHEET 31 MATH SKILLS

The Unit Factor and Dimensional Analysis

The measurements you take in science class, whether for time, mass, weight, or distance, are more than just numbers—they are also units. To make comparisons between measurements, it is convenient to have your measurements in the same units. A mathematical tool called a **unit factor** is used to convert back and forth between different kinds of units. A unit factor is a ratio that is equal to 1. Because it is equal to 1, multiplying a measurement by a unit factor changes the measurement's units but does not change its value. The skill of converting with a unit factor is known as **dimensional analysis.** Read on to see how it works.

Part 1: Converting with a Unit Factor

PROCEDURE: To convert units with a unit factor, determine the conversion factor between the units you have and the units you want to convert to. Then create the unit factor by making a ratio, in the form of a fraction, between the units you want to convert to in the numerator and the units you already have in the denominator. Finally, multiply your measurement by this unit factor to convert to the new units.

SAMPLE PROBLEM A: Convert 3.5 km to millimeters.

Step 1: Determine the conversion factor between kilometers and millimeters.

$$1 \text{ km} = 1{,}000{,}000 \text{ mm}$$

Step 2: Create the unit factor. Put the units you want to convert to in the numerator and the units you already have in the denominator.

$$\frac{1{,}000{,}000 \text{ mm}}{1 \text{ km}} = 1$$

Step 3: Multiply the unit factor by the measurement. Notice that the original unit of the measurement cancels out with the unit in the denominator of the unit factor, leaving the units you are converting to.

$$3.5 \cancel{\text{km}} \times \frac{1{,}000{,}000 \text{ mm}}{1 \cancel{\text{km}}} = \mathbf{3{,}500{,}000 \text{ mm}}$$

On Your Own!

1. Convert the following measurements using a unit factor:

Conversion	Unit factor	Answer
a. 2.34 cm = ? mm	$\frac{10 \text{ mm}}{1 \text{ cm}}$	23.4 mm
b. 54.6 mL = ? L	$\frac{1 \text{ L}}{1000 \text{ mL}}$	0.0546 L
c. 12 kg = ? g	$\frac{1000 \text{ g}}{1 \text{ kg}}$	12,000 g

Name ______________ Date ________ Class ________

Part 2: Working with Square Units

Many times in your science class, you will work with units of two dimensions, such as square centimeters (cm^2) or square kilometers (km^2). Dimensional analysis is especially useful when working with these types of units because it can help you to avoid confusing the different dimensions of your units. Carefully follow the steps in Sample Problem B to see how it works.

SAMPLE PROBLEM B: 1 km^2 is how many square meters?

Step 1: Simplify the units you are converting.

$$1\ km^2 = 1\ km \times 1\ km$$

Step 2: Create the unit factor for converting meters to kilometers. As in Sample Problem A, put the units you are converting *to* in the numerator.

$$\frac{1000\ m}{1\ km} = 1$$

Step 3: Multiply the measurement you are converting by the unit factor. Because 1 km^2 = 1 km × 1 km, you will need to multiply the measurement you are converting from by *two* unit factors. Notice that the original unit of measurement cancels the units in the denominator. This leaves the units you are converting *to*.

$$1\ km^2 \times \frac{1000\ m}{1\ km} \times \frac{1000\ m}{1\ km} = 1{,}000{,}000\ m \times m$$

$$1\ km^2 = \mathbf{1{,}000{,}000\ m^2}$$

Practice Your Skills!

2. Convert the following measurements:

Conversion	Unit factor	Answer
a. 3 cm^2 = ? m^2	$\frac{1\ m}{100\ cm}$	0.0003 m^2
b. 12,000 m^2 = ? km^2	$\frac{1\ km}{1000\ m}$	0.012 km^2
c. 980 cm^2 = ? mm^2	$\frac{10\ mm}{1\ cm}$	98,000 mm^2

3. An Olympic-sized soccer field has an area of 0.007776 km^2. How many square meters does a soccer field cover?

Unit factor: $\frac{1000\ m}{1\ km}$; $0.007776\ km^2 \times \frac{1000\ m}{1\ km} \times \frac{1000\ m}{1\ km} = 7776\ m^2$

MATH SKILLS

Name ______________ Date ________ Class ________

Working with Cubic Dimensions

Because volume can be measured by multiplying length times height times width, volume is expressed in units of three dimensions, or cubic units. Volume is often expressed in cubic millimeters (mm^3) or cubic centimeters (cm^3), but larger volumes may be expressed in cubic meters (m^3) or cubic kilometers (km^3). A cubic centimeter (cm^3) is equal to one milliliter (mL), and a cubic decimeter (dm^3) is equal to one liter (L). Doing dimensional analysis with cubic units is much like doing dimensional analysis with square units, except that with cubic units you will multiply the measurement you are converting by three unit factors instead of two. Follow the steps in Sample Problem C to see how it is done.

SAMPLE PROBLEM C: A certain plant needs about 525 cm^3 of soil to grow properly. How many cubic meters of soil is this?

Step 1: Simplify the units you are converting.

$$cm^3 = cm \times cm \times cm$$

Step 2: Create the unit factor for converting centimeters to meters, putting the units you are converting *to* in the numerator.

$$\frac{1\ m}{100\ cm}$$

Step 3: Multiply the measurement you are converting by the unit factors. Because cm^3 = cm × cm × cm, you will need to multiply the measurement you are converting from by *three* unit factors.

$$525\ cm^3 \times \frac{1\ m}{100\ cm} \times \frac{1\ m}{100\ cm} \times \frac{1\ m}{100\ cm} = 0.000525\ m \times m \times m$$

$$525\ cm^3 = \mathbf{0.000525\ m^3}$$

Try It Yourself!

4. Convert the following measurements:

Conversion	Unit factor	Answer
a. 30 m^3 = ? cm^3	$\frac{100\ cm}{1\ m}$	30,000,000 cm^3
b. 9000 mm^3 = ? m^3	$\frac{1\ m}{1000\ mm}$	0.000009 m^3
c. 4 km^3 = ? m^3	$\frac{1000\ m}{1\ km}$	4,000,000,000 m^3

Challenge Yourself!

5. The Mississippi River has an average water discharge of 17,000 m^3 per second. How many cubic kilometers of water does the river discharge in 1 hour? Show your work.

Unit factor: $\frac{1\ km}{1000\ m}$; $17{,}000\ m^3/s \times \frac{1\ km}{1000\ m} \times \frac{1\ km}{1000\ m} \times \frac{1\ km}{1000\ m} = 0.000017\ km^3/s$;

$0.000017\ km^3/s \times 60\ s/min = 0.00102\ km^3/min$; $0.00102\ km^3/min \times 60\ min/hr = 0.0612\ km^3/hr$

ANSWER KEY

Name ______________ Date ________ Class ________

WORKSHEET 32 — MATH IN SCIENCE: INTEGRATED SCIENCE

Math Skills Used: Multiplication, Division, Decimals

Density

Calculate density, and identify substances using a density chart.

Density is a measure of the amount of mass in a certain volume. This physical property is often used to identify and classify substances. It is usually expressed in grams per cubic centimeters, or g/cm³. The chart on the right lists the densities of some common materials.

Densities of Substances

Substance	Density (g/cm³)
Gold	19.3
Mercury	13.5
Lead	11.4
Iron	7.87
Aluminum	2.7
Bone	1.7–2.0
Gasoline	0.66–0.69
Air (dry)	0.00119

EQUATION: $\text{density} = \frac{\text{mass}}{\text{volume}}$

$D = \frac{m}{V}$

SAMPLE PROBLEM: What is the density of a billiard ball that has a volume of 100 cm³ and a mass of 250 g?

$D = \frac{250 \text{ g}}{100 \text{ cm}^3}$

$D = 2.5 \text{ g/cm}^3$

Your Turn!

1. A loaf of bread has a volume of 2270 cm³ and a mass of 454 g. What is the density of the bread?

   454 g ÷ 2270 cm³ = 0.2 g/cm³

2. A liter of water has a mass of 1000 g. What is the density of water? (Hint: 1 mL = 1 cm³)

   1000 g ÷ 1000 cm³ = 1 g/cm³

3. A block of wood has a density of 0.6 g/cm³ and a volume of 1.2 cm³. What is the mass of the block of wood? Be careful!

   0.6 g/cm³ × 1.2 cm³ = 0.72 g

4. Use the data below to calculate the density of each unknown substance. Then use the density chart above to determine the identity of each substance.

	Mass (g)	**Volume** (cm³)	**Density** (g/cm³)	**Substance**
Example:	4725	350	4725 ÷ 350 = 13.5	mercury
a.	171	15	171 ÷ 15 = 11.4	lead
b.	108	40	108 ÷ 40 = 2.7	aluminum
c.	475	250	475 ÷ 250 = 1.9	bone
d.	680	1000	680 ÷ 1000 = 0.68	gasoline

Name ______________ Date ________ Class ________

WORKSHEET 33 — MATH IN SCIENCE: INTEGRATED SCIENCE

Math Skills Used: Multiplication, Division, Decimals, Percentages, Geometry

The Pressure Is On!

Use math to learn about force and pressure.

You are under pressure! Even though you may not be aware of it, the air above you presses down on every square centimeter of your body with the weight of a 1.03 kg mass! Because water is so much denser than air, pressure in water is many times greater than this. **Pressure** is defined as the force exerted on a particular area. The unit for pressure is the pascal (Pa), which is the force one newton (N) exerts on one square meter (m²).

EQUATION: $\text{Pressure (Pa)} = \frac{\text{Force (N)}}{\text{Area (m}^2\text{)}}$

Apply Some Pressure!

Use the equation for pressure to answer the following questions:

1. An elephant that weighs 40,000 N stands on one leg during a circus performance. The area on the bottom of the elephant's foot is 0.4 m². How much pressure is exerted on the elephant's foot?

   40,000 N ÷ 0.4 m² = 100,000 Pa

2. A carpenter hammers a nail with a force of 45 N with every stroke. The head of the nail has a surface area of 0.002 m². How much pressure is exerted on the nailhead with each stroke?

   45 N ÷ 0.002 m² = 22,500 Pa

3. A brick falls from the third floor of a construction site. The brick hits the ground on its end, which measures 0.15 m by 0.25 m, with a force of 30 N. How much pressure is exerted by the brick on the ground? (Hint: Area of a rectangle = width × length)

   Area of rectangle = 0.15 m × 0.25 m = 0.0375 m²; 30 N ÷ 0.0375 m² = 800 Pa

Pressure in the Atmosphere

The air pressure we live under is about 101,000 Pa at sea level. Use this value to complete the following problems. Show all your work.

4. A mountain climber climbs to the top of Mt. Everest, which at 8848 m is the highest point on Earth. Because most of the air in the atmosphere is below this altitude, air pressure is about 50% less at the peak than at sea level. What is the air pressure exerted on the mountain climber?

   101,000 Pa × 0.5 = 50,500 Pa

5. A meteorologist reports that air pressure is reduced 8,585 Pa by an approaching hurricane. What percentage change from normal air pressure does this represent?

   8585 Pa ÷ 101,000 Pa = 0.085; since the new pressure is 8.5% of the previous pressure, this is a percentage change of 91.5%.

Name ______________ Date ________ Class ________

Pressure in the Ocean

Water pressure increases approximately 10,000 Pa for every 1 m of depth. That means that the pressure at the bottom of a swimming pool that is 10 m deep is almost as great as the pressure exerted by the entire atmosphere!

6. Use what you know about water pressure to complete the chart.

Water Pressure at Various Depths

Depth (m)	1	2	7.5	100	500	1500
Water pressure (Pa)	10,000	20,000	75,000	1,000,000	5,000,000	15,000,000

7. A sea turtle swims from a depth of 45 m to a depth of 28 m. What is the difference in water pressure between these two depths?

45 m − 28 m = 17 m; 17 × 10,000 Pa = 170,000 Pa

8. Deep Submergence Rescue Vehicles (DSRVs) can operate at depths of 4500 m.
   a. If a DSRV with a surface area of 16 m² goes to this depth, what is the total force on the entire hull of the sub?

   4500 × 10,000 = 45,000,000 Pa; 45,000,000 Pa × 16 m² = 720,000,000 N

   b. What would be the total force on a DSRV one-quarter that size at one-half that depth?

   4500 m ÷ 2 = 2250 m; 16 m² ÷ 4 = 4 m²; 2250 × 10,000 = 22,500,000 Pa;

   22,500,000 × 4 = 90,000,000 N

Challenge Yourself!

9. A magician lies on a bed of nails. The magician weighs 600 N and is supported by exactly 2000 nails. The tip of each nail has an area of 0.0001 m². Assuming that the weight of the magician is evenly distributed on the nails, how much pressure is exerted on each nail by the magician's body?

600 N ÷ 2000 nails = 0.3 N per nail; 0.3 N ÷ 0.0001 m² = 3000 Pa

Name ______________ Date ________ Class ________

WORKSHEET 34 MATH IN SCIENCE: INTEGRATED SCIENCE

MATH SKILLS USED: Multiplication, Division, Decimals

Sound Reasoning

Use your math skills to understand dolphin echolocation.

Dolphins use echolocation to find their way through murky waters. They do this by emitting a clicking sound and listening for an echo. The direction and delay of the echo give the dolphins information about what objects are nearby and where the objects are located.

1. Sound travels about 1530 m/s in sea water. How many times faster does sound travel in sea water than in air? (The speed of sound in air at 25°C is about 345 m/s.)

1530 m/s ÷ 345 m/s = 4.43; Sound travels 4.43 times faster in sea water than in air.

2. A dolphin emits a click that is reflected off an object. If it takes 0.2 seconds for the sound to be sent and to come back, how far away is the object?

0.2 s ÷ 2 = 0.1 s; The sound took 0.1 seconds to reach the object.

0.1 s × 1530 m/s = 153 m; The object is 153 m away.

3. How long would it take the sound to be sent and returned from the same object in air?

The sound must travel a total distance of 153 m × 2 = 306 meters. At 345 m/s, this would require 306 m ÷ 345 m/s = 0.89 seconds. Note that this is 4.43 times longer than in sea water because the speed of sound is 4.43 times faster in sea water than in air.

4. Assume that the speed of sound decreases by 6 m/s for every 10°C decrease in water temperature. If a dolphin swam to the Arctic Ocean, where the water is about 5°C, how would the dolphin's ability to estimate the distance to an object be affected?

The dolphin would think objects were farther away than they actually would be. Suppose that the dolphin uses the speed of sound in sea water and a return time of 0.5 seconds for an echo off an object. The dolphin would think that the object was 1530 m/s × 0.25 s = 382.5 m away. The speed of sound in the Arctic Ocean (20°C colder) is 1530 m/s − (6 m/s × 2) = 1518 m/s, so the object would actually be 1518 m/s × 0.25 s = 379.5 m away.

Name ______________ Date ________ Class ________

WORKSHEET 35 MATH IN SCIENCE: INTEGRATED SCIENCE

Using Temperature Scales

MATH SKILLS USED: Addition, Multiplication, Fractions, Decimals, Scientific Notation

Convert between degrees Fahrenheit and degrees Celsius.

Do you remember the last time you had your temperature taken? Your body temperature is usually about 98.6°F. This temperature is in degrees Fahrenheit (°F). The Fahrenheit temperature scale is a common temperature scale. In science class, however, a scale known as the Celsius (°C) scale is used. Temperatures in one scale can be mathematically converted to the other system using one of the equations below.

EQUATIONS: Conversion from Fahrenheit to Celsius: $\frac{5}{9} \times (°F - 32) = °C$

Conversion from Celsius to Fahrenheit: $\frac{9}{5} \times °C + 32 = °F$

SAMPLE PROBLEMS:

A. Convert 59°F to degrees Celcius.

$°C = \frac{5}{9} \times (°F - 32)$

$°C = \frac{5}{9} \times (59 - 32)$

$°C = \frac{5}{9} \times 27$

$°C = \mathbf{15°C}$

B. Convert 112°C to degrees Fahrenheit.

$°F = \frac{9}{5} \times °C + 32$

$°F = \frac{9}{5} \times 112 + 32$

$°F = 201\frac{3}{5} + 32$

$°F = \mathbf{233\frac{3}{5}°F}$

Turn Up the Temperature!

1. Convert the following temperatures from degrees Fahrenheit to degrees Celsius:

a. 98.6°F $\frac{5}{9} \times (98.6 - 32) = 37°C$

b. 482°F $\frac{5}{9} \times (482 - 32) = 250°C$

c. −4°F $\frac{5}{9} \times (-4 - 32) = -20°C$

2. Convert the following temperatures from degrees Celsius to degrees Fahrenheit:

a. 24°C $\frac{9}{5} \times 24 + 32 = 43\frac{1}{5} + 32 = 75\frac{1}{5}°F$

b. 17°C $\frac{9}{5} \times 17 + 32 = 30\frac{3}{5} + 32 = 62\frac{3}{5}°F$

c. 0°C $\frac{9}{5} \times 0 + 32 = 0 + 32 = 32°F$

Challenge Yourself!

3. Convert 2.7×10^4°C to degrees Fahrenheit. $\frac{9}{5} \times 27{,}000 + 32 = 48{,}600 + 32 = 48{,}632°F$

Name ______________ Date ________ Class ________

WORKSHEET 36 MATH IN SCIENCE: INTEGRATED SCIENCE

Radioactive Decay and the Half-life

MATH SKILLS USED: Multiplication, Division, Fractions, Decimals, Percentages, Scientific Notation

Use the half-lives of elements to learn about radioactive dating.

Most elements found in nature are stable; they do not change over time. Some elements, however, are unstable—that is, they change into a different element over time. Elements that go through this process of change are called **radioactive**, and the process of transformation is called **radioactive decay.** Because radioactive decay happens very steadily, scientists can use radioactive elements like clocks to measure the passage of time. By looking at how much of a certain element remains in an object and how much of it has decayed, scientists can determine an approximate age for the object.

So why are scientists interested in learning the ages of objects? By looking at very old things, such as rocks and fossils, and determining when they were formed, scientists learn about the history of the Earth and the plants and animals that have lived here. Radioactive dating makes this history lesson possible! A **half-life** is the time that it takes for half a certain amount of a radioactive material to decay, and it can range from less than a second to billions of years. The chart below lists the half-lives of some radioactive elements.

Table of Half-lives

Element	Half-life	Element	Half-life
Bismuth-212	60.5 minutes	Phosphorous-24	14.3 days
Carbon-14	5730 years	Polonium-215	0.0018 seconds
Chlorine-36	400,000 years	Radium-226	1600 years
Cobalt-60	5.26 years	Sodium-24	15 hours
Iodine-131	8.07 days	Uranium-238	4.5 billion years

1. Use the data in the table above to complete the following chart:

Table of Remaining Radium

Number of years after formation	0	1600	3200	6400	12,800
Percent of radium-226 remaining	100%	50%	25%	12.5%	6.25%

2. If 1 g of sodium-24 has decayed from a sample that was originally 2 g, how old is the sample?

Because half of the sample has decayed, we know that one half-life has passed, which is 15 hours.

The sample is 15 hours old.

3. What fraction of chlorine-36 remains undecayed after 200,000 years?

200,000 is one-half of 400,000, so one-half of the half-life has passed. Therefore, one-quarter of the sample has decayed, leaving three-quarters of the sample undecayed.

Name ______________ Date ________ Class ________

4. As uranium-238 decays, it becomes lead-206. After 3.5 g of uranium-238 decays for 1.125×10^9 years, how many grams of the sample will be lead-206?

$(1.125 \times 10^9) \div (4.5 \times 10^9) = 0.25$ of the half-life has passed. Therefore, 0.125 g of the sample has decayed. $0.125 \times 3.5 = 0.438$; 0.438 g of the sample has decayed into lead-206.

5. A scientist has a 2.5 g sample of radium-226. How many grams of the sample will decay in 800 years?

$800 \div 1600 = 0.5$; 0.5 of the half-life passes in 800 years. Therefore, 0.25 of the sample decays in this time. $0.25 \times 2.5 = 0.625$ g of radium-226 will decay in 800 years.

6. An archaeologist finds a piece of old bone that she believes may be 2000 years old. The lab technician tells her that the carbon-14 in the bone has completed 25 percent of its first half-life. Does this finding support her belief about the age of the bone? Why or why not?

25% of the half-life of carbon-14 is 0.25×5730 years $= 1432.5$ years; Because the bone is less than 2000 years old, this finding does not support her belief.

7. A technician does a test on an unidentified radioactive element and discovers that it has a half-life of 4.5×10^9 years. What element do you think it is, and why?

4.5×10^9 years is 4.5 billion years; The substance may be uranium-238, which has the same half-life.

8. A paleontologist unearths the remains of a *Tyrannosaurus rex*. We know that these dinosaurs became extinct about 65 million years ago. Therefore, would it be reasonable to expect that the carbon-14 in the fossil has completed 15,000 half-lives? Why or why not?

$15{,}000 \times 5730 = 85{,}950{,}000$ years; Yes, it would be reasonable because the *T. rex* had not yet become extinct 85 million years ago.

Name ______________ Date ________ Class ________

WORKSHEET 37 MATH IN SCIENCE: INTEGRATED SCIENCE

Rain-Forest Math

MATH SKILLS USED
- Multiplication
- Decimals
- Percentages
- Scientific Notation
- The Unit Factor and Dimensional Analysis

Calculate the damage to the world's rain forests.

Tropical rain forests now cover about 7 percent of the Earth's land surface; however, about half the original forests have been cut during the last 50 years. An additional 2 percent of the total remaining tropical rain forest is being cut each year.

The Damage Done

1. Approximately what percentage of the Earth's surface was covered by rain forest 50 years ago?

$0.07 \times 2 = 0.14 = 14\%$; Approximately 14% of the Earth's surface was covered by rain forest 50 years ago.

2. The land surface of the Earth is approximately 1.49×10^8 km². How many square kilometers of that is rain forest today? Give your answer in scientific notation.

$(1.49 \times 10^8) \times (1.49 \times 10^8) \times 0.07 = 1.04 \times 10^7$; 1.04×10^7 km² of the Earth's surface is covered by rain forest.

3. Suppose a certain rain forest consists of 500,000 km². The amount of rainfall per square meter per day is 20 L. If 2 percent of this rain forest is cut this year, how much water will be lost to next year's water cycle? Show all your work.

Amount of rain forest lost this year $= 500{,}000\ km^2 \times 0.02 = 10{,}000\ km^2$; unit conversion: $1\ km^2 = 1000\ m \times 1000\ m = 1{,}000{,}000\ m^2$; water lost per day $= 10{,}000\ km^2 \times \frac{1{,}000{,}000\ m^2}{1\ km^2} \times \frac{20\ L}{1\ m^2} = 200{,}000{,}000{,}000\ L$.

Amount of water lost this year $= \frac{200{,}000{,}000{,}000\ L}{1\ day} \times \frac{365\ days}{1\ year} = 73{,}000{,}000{,}000{,}000\ L$.

ANSWER KEY

Name ______________ Date ________ Class ________

WORKSHEET 38 MATH IN SCIENCE: LIFE SCIENCE

MATH SKILLS USED: Addition, Subtraction

Knowing Nutrition

Use a Calorie chart and an activity chart to learn about how we consume and burn the energy in food.

The food we eat provides the energy we need to work, play, and stay healthy. The energy in food is measured in **calories (cal)**, which is the thermal energy required to raise the temperature of 1 g of water 1°C. Because a single calorie is such a small amount of energy, nutritionists and food makers use the **kilocalorie (C)**, or 1,000 calories, to measure the energy in food and drinks. The number of Calories a person needs to consume each day depends largely on his or her body size and level of activity. The more active a person is, the more Calories he or she needs to keep going. The chart below shows Calorie counts for single servings of some common foods.

Calorie Count

Food	C	Food	C
Apple	81	Low-fat milk	90
American cheese	105	Orange juice	112
Baked potato with sour cream	393	Pancake	61
Baked chicken, white meat	142	Pancake syrup	50
Wheat bread	70	Peanut butter	188
Carrots	31	Cheese pizza	140
Cola	152	Scrambled egg	100
Corn flakes	100	Spaghetti	260
French fries	235	Vanilla ice cream	184
Plain hamburger	275	Vegetable soup	78

Counting Your Calories

1. Use the data in the Calorie chart to calculate the total number of Calories consumed in each of the following meals. Be sure to show your work.

a. **Breakfast**
2 scrambled eggs
1 slice of bread
1 glass of orange juice
1 pancake

2 scrambled eggs = 100 + 100 = 200
1 slice of bread = 70
1 glass of orange juice = 112
1 pancake = 61
Calorie total = 443

b. **Lunch**
1 peanut-butter sandwich (2 slices of bread)
1 bowl of soup
1 apple
1 cola

1 peanut-butter sandwich = 188 + 70 + 70 = 328
1 bowl of soup = 78
1 apple = 81
1 cola = 152
Calorie total = 639

Name ______________ Date ________ Class ________

c. **Dinner**
1 baked potato
2 pieces of chicken
1 glass of milk
2 servings of carrots
1 ice cream

1 baked potato = 393
2 pieces of chicken = 142 + 142 = 284
1 glass of milk = 90
2 carrots = 31 + 31 = 62
1 ice cream = 184
Calorie total = 1013

2. How many Calories were consumed in the entire day?

443 + 639 + 1013 = 2095 Calories consumed in the day

Activity Chart

The following chart shows the approximate number of Calories burned in half an hour of exercise. Note that calories burned varies with a person's mass and type of excercise.

Calories Burned Per Half Hour of Excercise

	Body mass (kg)				
Activity	32–42	43–49	50–57	58–66	67–75
Basketball	123	155	195	240	280
Bicycling	185	225	260	300	340
Bowling	30	35	39	45	52
Jogging	243	287	330	385	440
Skating	96	108	120	135	149
Soccer	156	186	220	266	312
Swimming	182	215	248	292	336
Volleyball	150	173	195	225	255
Walking	108	126	144	168	192

Hint: To convert weight in pounds (lb) to mass in kilograms (kg), multiply pounds by 0.45.

Use the data from the activity chart above to answer the following questions:

3. How many Calories does a 55 kg person burn in half an hour of swimming, half an hour of playing basketball, and an hour of walking?

(248 + 195 + 144 + 144) = 731; 731 C

4. How many fewer Calories are burned in half an hour of bowling by a 74 kg person than in half an hour of jogging by a 40 kg person?

243 − 52 = 191; The bowler burns 191 fewer Calories than the jogger.

Name ______________ Date ______ Class ______

Knowing Nutrition, continued

5. A 44 kg girl eats a lunch of a hamburger with cheese, a serving of French fries, and a cola. Would an hour of jogging burn off the Calories she consumed?

   lunch: 275 + 105 + 235 + 152 = 767 C; jogging: 287 +287 = 574 C burned; No, an hour of jogging would not burn off the Calories from lunch.

6. The "special of the day" at the cafeteria is one piece of baked chicken, a bowl of soup, carrots, and a glass of milk. You know that you will be skating after school for one hour. Assuming that you have a mass of 66 kg, will this meal give you enough energy for your workout?

   lunch: 142 + 78 + 31 + 90 = 341 C; skating: 135 + 135 = 270 C; Yes, it will give you enough energy.

7. How long would a 64 kg person have to play volleyball to burn 450 C?

   225 + 225 = 450 C burned; A 64 kg person would have to play volleyball for one hour to burn 450 C.

8. How many more Calories does a 41 kg person burn in half an hour of jogging than a 60 kg person who spends the same amount of time walking?

   jogging: 243 C; walking: 168 C; 243 − 168 = 75; The jogger burns 75 more Calories than the walker.

9. After an hour of playing basketball, two 75 kg members of the team go out to lunch. They each consume two hamburgers and a cola. How many more Calories did they consume than burn?

   total C burned: 280 + 280 + 280 + 280 = 1120;

   total C consumed: 275 + 275 +275 +275 + 152 + 152 = 1404; 1404 − 1120 = 284;

   They consumed 284 more Calories than they burned.

Long-term Challenge

10. Design a three-day menu for yourself, and calculate the total number of Calories you would consume. Then design an exercise program that burns approximately the same number of Calories as you consume. Use a variety of different foods and physical activities in your plans.

Name ______________ Date ______ Class ______

WORKSHEET 39 MATH IN SCIENCE: LIFE SCIENCE

Random Samples: Estimating Population

MATH SKILLS USED
Addition
Subtraction
Multiplication
Division
Averages
Fractions
Percentages
Geometry

Use your math skills to learn about the use and accuracy of random population samples.

"Why did we bother with a picnic anyway? These ants are everywhere," Gina complained. "There must be a million ants on our blanket!" Dylan agreed. Of course, Gina and Dylan were exaggerating. But suppose they really did want to know how many ants were in the park. How could they find out? Counting each ant would be very difficult; ants are tiny, and they live in a large area, have a large population, and move around a lot. To solve this problem, Gina and Dylan could use a mathematical tool called a **random sample** to estimate the total population of ants in the park. To take a random sample, they would count the ants in a particular region of the park. To estimate the total population of ants in the park, they would first divide the total area of the park by the area of the sample region. Then they would multiply that number by the number of ants they counted in the random sample.

The following diagram shows the section of the park where Gina and Dylan had their picnic. Each dot represents 25 ants. Use the diagram to answer the questions.

	A	B	C	D	E
1	••	•••	•	••••	•
2	•••		••••	•••	••••
3	••••	••••	•••••	••	
4		•••	••	•	•••
5	••		••••		•••••

1. Each square on the grid represents 1 m^2 of the picnic area. What is the size of the picnic area?

   1 $m^2 \times 25 = 25$ m^2; The picnic area is 25 m^2.

Taking a Random Sample

In order to get a closer population estimate, count the number of ants in a selection of squares that are chosen at random. Then answer the following questions. Each square can be identified by a letter and a number. For example, the first square at the top left is square A1.

ANSWER KEY

Name ______ Date ______ Class ______

Random Samples: Estimating Population, continued

2. The following is a randomly chosen selection of squares. Calculate the number of ants found in each of these squares. (1 dot = 25 ants)

a. D2 $3 \times 25 = 75$ b. E4 $3 \times 25 = 75$
c. E2 $4 \times 25 = 100$ d. B1 $3 \times 25 = 75$
e. D3 $2 \times 25 = 50$ f. C5 $4 \times 25 = 100$
g. C3 $5 \times 25 = 125$ h. A4 $0 \times 25 = 0$

3. What is the average number of ants per square meter in the sampled area?

$(75 + 75 + 100 + 75 + 50 + 100 + 125 + 0) \div 8 = 75$; The average number of ants per m^2 is 75.

4. Using the average from item 3, estimate the ants' total population.

$75 \times 25 = 1875$; The estimated population is 1875 ants.

How Accurate Was the Estimated Population?

You can check the accuracy of the estimated population by finding the **percent error.** The closer your percent error is to zero, the more accurate your estimate is. In order to calculate the percent error, you must know the exact population, so count all of the dots to find the exact population of the ants before continuing.

5. Use the following equation to find the percent error of your estimate. (Hint: If the value you determine by subtracting the exact population from the estimated population is negative, use the absolute value in your calculations.)

$$\text{percent error} = \frac{\text{estimated population} - \text{exact population}}{\text{exact population}} \times 100$$

exact population = $60 \times 25 = 1500$ ants;

$\frac{1875 - 1500}{1500} \times 100 = \frac{375}{1500} \times 100 = \frac{3}{12} \times 100 = 25\%$

6. Make a random selection of five squares from the grid, and determine the estimated population based on your random sample. Then calculate the percent error as you did in question 5. How does your percent error compare with the percent error found in question 5?

Sample answer: C4, B5, D4, E2, B4; average number of ants = 50;

estimated population: $50 \times 25 = 1250$ ants; $\frac{1875 - 1250}{1250} \times 100 = \frac{625}{1250} \times 100 = \frac{1}{2} \times 100 = 50\%$;

This is twice the percent error calculated in question 5.

Name ______ Date ______ Class ______

WORKSHEET 40 MATH IN SCIENCE: LIFE SCIENCE

MATH SKILLS USED
Multiplication
Decimals
Percentages

Punnett Square Popcorn

Use the Punnett Square to learn about dominance and codominance in inherited traits.

You are a cofounder of Flav-R-Gro, Inc., a company that specializes in creating genetically engineered foods. You and your partner, Maisie Mantequilla, have recently been concentrating on developing new types of corn. Together, you have developed a type of corn that, fresh from the stalk, tastes like it has been roasted with just the perfect amount of butter and salt! Your new creation, which you and Maisie call WonderCorn, is bringing you the admiration of your peers and the loyalty of customers. Hungry corn consumers are eager to try your tasty creation because they can eat it without worrying about the health risks caused by adding butter and salt to food. You and Maisie succeeded through determination, hard work, and an understanding of *codominance.*

Background

In some cases of genetic inheritance, two dominant traits are expressed together instead of one trait being dominant and one trait being recessive. This phenomenon is known as **codominance.** When codominance occurs, both traits are evident in the phenotype. For example, a cross between a homozygous red horse and a homozygous white horse results in offspring with a roan coat, which consists of both red hairs and white hairs. Human blood types are also determined by codominant traits.

You and Maisie suspected that the taste trait in corn was codominant. To find out, you crossed two other types of corn that you created: a homozygous salty corn (*SS*) and a homozygous buttery corn (*BB*). The offspring were all WonderCorn. See the Punnett square below for this cross.

	B	*B*
S	*SB*	*SB*
S	*SB*	*SB*

Solve the Punnet Problems!

1. What is the genotype of WonderCorn?

SB

2. What percentage of the offspring have this genotype?

100%

Name ______________ Date ________ Class ________

Punnett Square Popcorn, continued

Your hunch about the codominant taste traits was right. You and Maisie then did another Punnett square to predict the offspring that would be produced by a second-generation (heterozygous) cross. Complete the cross in the Punnett square below.

	S	*B*
S	*SS*	*SB*
B	*SB*	*BB*

3. What percentage of these offspring will be WonderCorn?

50% will be WonderCorn.

4. What percentage of these offspring could you and Maisie use for another homozygous cross?

50% could be used for another homozygous cross.

5. If the heterozygous cross produces 736 offspring, how many will be WonderCorn? Show your work.

$736 \times 0.5 = 368$

6. How many of the 736 offspring will taste salty but not buttery? Show your work.

$736 \times 0.25 = 184$; $\frac{1}{4}$ will be salty but not buttery.

7. The demand for WonderCorn has been high! Grover's Grocery alone has ordered 50 bushels for delivery as soon as possible. Flav-R-Gro, Inc., is fresh out of WonderCorn, but you and Maisie are beginning another growing cycle. Would you be better off using a homozygous cross or a heterozygous cross to fill the order for Grover's Grocery? Explain your answer.

You would be better off using a homozygous cross because all of the offspring of a homozygous cross will be WonderCorn.

Name ______________ Date ________ Class ________

WORKSHEET 41 MATH IN SCIENCE: LIFE SCIENCE

MATH SKILLS USED
Multiplication
Division
Decimals
SI Measurement and Conversion

Scale of Organisms

Use the SI system to compare the sizes of some of the smallest and largest organisms on Earth.

Mass is the amount of matter that composes an object or living thing. Look at the scale showing the range of masses of living things. Each division of the scale represents a factor of 10, in terms of the mass of the organism. For example, the blue whale, which is the largest animal alive today, is three divisions above a human. Its mass is therefore $10 \times 10 \times 10$ (or 1000 times) the mass of a human. In the same way, a human has a mass 1000 times that of a parakeet.

Use the scale to complete the following exercises:

1. The parakeet has a mass 1000 times that of what other living thing?

A fly

2. A large protist has a mass 1000 times that of a small protist.

3. A *Salmonella* bacterium has a mass 1000 times that of a mycoplasma.

4. A small protist has a mass 1,000,000 times that of a mycoplasma.

5. A human has a mass 1,000,000,000 times greater than a large protist.

6. A fly's mass is 1,000,000,000 times greater than a *Salmonella* bacterium.

7. A blue whale is 25 m long, while a mycoplasma is 0.3 µm long. How many mycoplasmas placed end to end would stretch from one end of the whale to the other?

$25 \div 0.0000003 = 83{,}333{,}333$

Name ________________ Date ________ Class ________

WORKSHEET 42 MATH IN SCIENCE: EARTH SCIENCE

Sedimentation in the Grand Canyon

MATH SKILLS USED
Multiplication
Division
Decimals
Percentages
SI Measurement and Conversion
Geometry

Use your math skills to study the Colorado River's rate of sedimentation in the Grand Canyon.

Imagine that you are a geologist and that you read the following excerpt in a geological journal:

> **EARTH ALERT:** A gradual change in the global climate is causing the Colorado River to slowly deposit sediment in the Grand Canyon. Scientists estimate that the present rate of deposition is raising the canyon floor by 0.05 mm per year.

Your geological interests lead you to ask some questions. Suppose that you've organized your questions and concerns into the following itemized list. Using your mathematical knowledge, answer the following six items about the fate of the Grand Canyon.

Question List

ITEM 1: If the canyon is 1500 m deep, how long will it be until the river completely fills the canyon with sediment? Show your work.

The canyon is 1500 m, or 1,500,000 mm, deep. If the rate of sediment deposit is 0.05 mm/y, then it would take 1,500,000 mm ÷ 0.05 mm/y = 30,000,000 years for the canyon to be completely filled with sediment.

ITEM 2: Make a graph on the grid below to show the amount of sediment deposited in the Grand Canyon over an average human lifetime (about 75 years in the United States). Make sure to label the *x*-axis and *y*-axis and to give your graph a title.

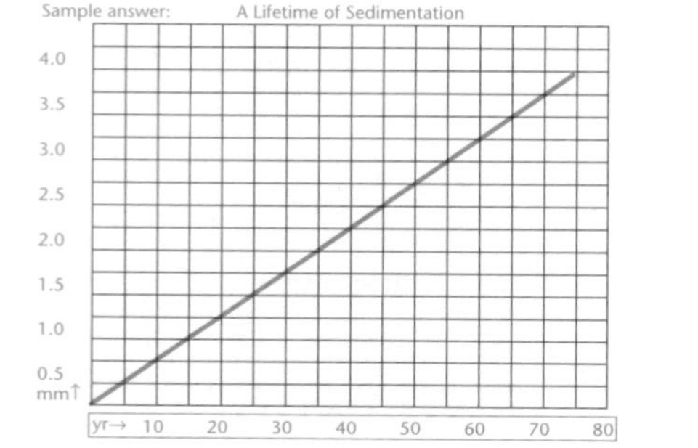

Name ________________ Date ________ Class ________

ITEM 3: Some geologists believe that the sedimentation rate of the Colorado River could increase in the future. If the rate of deposition increases by 40%, how much does the river deposit per year?

Forty percent of 0.05 mm is 0.4 × 0.05 = 0.02. The total deposition of the river would then be 0.05 + 0.02 = 0.07 mm/y.

ITEM 4: What will be the total volume of sediment dumped into the canyon if the canyon is 2 km wide and 30 km long? Show your work.

The dimensions of the canyon are 2 km × 30 km × 1.5 km (the depth of the canyon is 1500 m, or 1.5 km, from Item 1). 2 km × 30 km × 1.5 km = 90 km³. The volume of the sediment that fills up the canyon is 90 km³.

ITEM 5: If the same amount of sediment from Item 4 were instead carried to the mouth of the river and dumped into the ocean, a delta would form. Assuming that the ocean is 500 m deep at the mouth of the river and that the elevation of the new land at the delta is at sea level, what will be the surface area of the delta? Show your work. (Hint: area = volume ÷ depth)

Area of the delta = volume of sediment ÷ depth of ocean; 90 km³ ÷ 0.5 km = 180 km²

Critical Thinking Challenge

ITEM 6: An animal is buried by the sediment at the bottom of the canyon. If a fossil hunter finds the animal 1 million years after the canyon is completely filled, how old will the fossil be? Explain your answer.

The animal is buried in the sediment at the bottom of the canyon, so (based on Item 1) its fossilized form would be 30 million years old by the time the canyon completely filled with sediment. If a fossil hunter finds the fossil one million years after the canyon is filled, the fossil is 31 million years old.

Name ______________ Date ________ Class ________

WORKSHEET 43 **MATH IN SCIENCE: EARTH SCIENCE**

MATH SKILLS USED
Addition
Percentages
Powers of 10

Earthquake Power!

Use the Richter scale to compare the size and magnitude of earthquakes.

Sometimes earthquakes are strong enough to cause a huge amount of damage—highways crumble and buildings fall in an instant. Other times, earthquakes can be so slight that people hardly feel them. Scientists use a mathematical system called the Richter scale to compare the size and magnitude of earthquakes. An earthquake's magnitude depends on the amplitude of seismic waves, which are recorded by a seismograph. The greater the amplitude of the waves is, the higher the reading on the Richter scale is.

Part 1: Richter Readings

Earthquakes per year	Magnitude on the Richter scale*	Severity
1	8.0 and higher	great
18	7.0–7.9	major
120	6.0–6.9	strong
800	5.0–5.9	moderate
6200	4.0–4.9	light
49,000	3.0–3.9	minor

*Earthquakes measuring less than 3.0 are not included because approximately 9000 occur daily.

Use What You Know!

Use the table above to answer the following questions. Remember to show your work.

1. In a given year, how many earthquakes measure 6.0 or greater?

$120 + 18 + 1 = 139$; In a given year, 139 earthquakes measure 6.0 or greater.

2. In a given year, what percentage of earthquakes measure 3.0 or greater are moderate?

Total number measuring 3.0 or greater = $1 + 18 + 120 + 800 + 6200 + 49{,}000 = 56{,}139$;
percentage of moderate earthquakes = $800 \div 56{,}139 = 0.014 = 1.4\%$

3. Calculate the percentage of earthquakes that measure 5.0 or greater that are classified as "major" and "great."

Number of earthquakes measuring 5.0 or greater = $800 + 120 + 18 + 1 = 939$. Percentage of these that are "major" and "great" = $(18 + 1) \div 939 = 0.02 = 2\%$

Name ______________ Date ________ Class ________

Earthquake Power! continued

Part 2: Richter Math

The Richter scale is based on a mathematical system. Each whole-number increase in magnitude on the Richter scale represents an increase in measured amplitude by a factor of 10. That means that an earthquake measuring 4.0 on the Richter scale is 10 times as strong as an earthquake measuring 3.0.

The Richter scale is also used to estimate the relative energy released by earthquakes. Each whole-number increase on the Richter scale represents an increase in energy release by a factor of 32. Examine the table below, and work the problems that follow. Be sure to show your work.

The Richter Scale

Difference in magnitude	Relative strength	Change of energy released
0.3	2.0 times as strong	3 times as much
0.5	3.2 times as strong	5.5 times as much
1	10 (10^1) times as strong	32 times as much
2	100 (10^2) times as strong	32^2 times as much
3	1000 (10^3) times as strong	32^3 times as much
4	10,000 (10^4) times as strong	32^4 times as much
5	100,000 (10^5) times as strong	32^5 times as much

4. On December 16, 1920, an earthquake measuring 8.6 on the Richter scale hit Gansu, a province in China. Twelve years later, an earthquake measuring 7.6 hit Gansu. How much stronger was the 1920 earthquake?

$8.6 - 7.6 = 1$; The 1920 earthquake was 10 times stronger.

5. How much more energy did the 1920 earthquake release compared with the second earthquake?

The 1920 earthquake released 32 times as much energy.

6. In 1906, an earthquake occurred in San Francisco that measured 8.3 on the Richter scale. In 1994, an earthquake occurred in Northridge, California, that measured 6.7 on the Richter scale.

a. How much stronger was the San Francisco earthquake?

$8.3 - 6.7 = 1.6$, or $1 + 0.3 + 0.3$; The San Francisco earthquake was $10 \times 2 \times 2 = 40$ times stronger.

b. How much more energy did the San Francisco earthquake release?

$32 \times 3 \times 3 = 288$; It released 288 times more energy.

ANSWER KEY

Name ______________________ Date ____________ Class ____________

WORKSHEET 44

MATH IN SCIENCE: EARTH SCIENCE

Distances in Space

MATH SKILLS USED
Multiplication
Division
Decimals
Scientific Notation
SI Measurement and Conversion

Learn about the units of length used to measure distances in our solar system and beyond.

Because astronomers study objects over such extremely large distances, astronomers commonly use units of length that are much bigger than the ones we usually use. Two common units of distance used in astronomy are the astronomical unit (AU) and the light-year.

Astronomical Unit

The astronomical unit (AU) is the average distance from the Earth to the sun, measured to be about 1.5×10^8 km. It is a convenient unit to use when discussing distances within our solar system.

1. Saturn has an average distance of 9.5 AU from the sun. How many centimeters is this?

   $9.5 \text{ AU} = 9.5 \times (1.5 \times 10^8 \text{ km}) = 1.425 \times 10^9 \text{ km}$; $1.425 \times 10^9 \text{ km} = 1.425 \times 10^{14}$ cm, or 142,500,000,000,000 cm

2. Pluto, the outermost planet in the solar system, is about 6×10^9 km from the sun. How many astronomical units (AU) is this?

   $(6 \times 10^9) \div (1.5 \times 10^8) = 40$ AU

Light-year

The light-year is defined as the distance that light travels in a year. (The speed of light is 3×10^5 km/s.) For instance, Alpha Centauri, the closest star to the Earth after the sun, is 4.3 light-years from us.

3. How long does it take light from this star to reach us?

   It takes 4.3 years.

4. The star Betelgeuse, meaning "armpit of the giant," is 310 light-years from Earth. How many hours does light from this star take to reach Earth?

   310×365 days/year = 113,150 days; 113,150 days $\times$ 24 hours = 2,715,600 hours

5. How many AUs are in a light-year? (*Hint:* There are approximately 31,536,000 seconds in a year.)

   Light travels 3×10^5 km/s $\times$ 31,536,000 seconds $= 9.5 \times 10^{12}$ km in 1 year.

   There are $(9.5 \times 10^{12}) \div (1.5 \times 10^8) = 6.3 \times 10^4$ AU, or 63,000 AU in a light-year.

Name ______________________ Date ____________ Class ____________

WORKSHEET 45

MATH IN SCIENCE: EARTH SCIENCE

Geologic Time Scale

MATH SKILLS USED
Subtraction
Division
Decimals
Percentages
Scientific Notation

Understand geologic time using the geologic time scale.

If you wanted to find out how long it has been since your last birthday, you would simply look at a yearly calendar, right? But what would you do if you wanted to find out how long ago a dinosaur lived or a volcano was formed? Then you would need a calendar that goes much farther back in time—maybe all the way back to the beginning of Earth's history. There is such a calendar—it is called the **geologic time scale.** It begins about 4.6 billion years ago and continues up to the present. Instead of months and days, it divides Earth's history into *eons, eras,* and *periods.*

Geologic Time Scale

Eon	Era	Period	Millions of years ago
Phanerozoic	Cenozoic	Quaternary	1.8
		Tertiary	65
	Mesozoic	Cretaceous	144
		Jurassic	206
		Triassic	248
	Paleozoic	Permian	290
		Pennsylvanian	323
		Mississippian	354
		Devonian	417
		Silurian	443
		Ordovician	490
		Cambrian	540
Proterozoic			2500
Archean			3800
Hadean			4600

It's Been a Long, Long Time . . .

1. Calculate the number of years that each era and eon lasted, starting with the present era.

   Cenozoic, 65 million years; Mesozoic, $248 - 65 = 183$ million years; Paleozoic, $540 - 248 = 292$ million years; Proterozoic, $2500 - 540 = 1960$ million years; Archean, $3800 - 2500 = 1300$ million years; Hadean, $4600 - 3800 = 800$ million years

2. How many years passed between the end of the Pennsylvanian period and the beginning of the Tertiary period? Be careful!

   $290 - 65 = 225$ million years passed

Name ____________ Date ________ Class ________

Managing Huge Numbers

The geologic time scale measures extremely long periods of time. When numbers are very large, it is often easier to do calculations or comparisons using scientific notation, which simplifies large numbers.

3. Write the following times in scientific notation:

a. the beginning of the Quaternary period 1.8×10^6

b. the end of the Proterozoic eon 5.4×10^8

c. the beginning of the Earth's history 4.6×10^9

d. the beginning of the Jurassic period 2.06×10^8

e. the end of the Jurassic period 1.44×10^8

4. The Archean eon lasted 1.3×10^9 years. The era in which we live, the Cenozoic, meaning "recent life," has lasted 6.5×10^7 years. How many times longer was the Archean eon than the present era?

$(1.3 \times 10^9) \div (6.5 \times 10^7) = 20$ times longer

The Fossil Record

As plants and animals appeared and disappeared from the Earth, they left a fossil record. In fact, the divisions in the geologic time scale are based on distinct changes in the fossil record. For example, the extinction of the dinosaurs separates the Mesozoic era from the Cenozoic era. In the chart below, you can see that the appearance of different living things characterizes different periods in the Earth's history.

Animals in the Fossil Record

Animals	First appearance
Birds	Jurassic period (late)
Mammals	Jurassic period (early)
Reptiles	Pennsylvanian period
Amphibians	Mississippian period
Fishes	Ordovician period

5. Approximately how much longer have fishes been on Earth than mammals?

490 million years − 206 million years = 284 million years longer

Name ____________ Date ________ Class ________

6. The earliest plant life began to appear on land during the Silurian period, about 420 million years ago. During approximately what percentage of the total history of the Earth were plants *not* growing on land?

$(4.2 \times 10^8) \div (4.6 \times 10^9) = 0.091 = 9.1\%$; $100\% - 9.1\% = 90.9\%$

Calendar Challenge

Another way to understand the geologic time scale is to picture Earth's history as it would appear on a typical calendar. To begin, determine how many years a "day" is in geologic time. Then determine in which months the eras fall. Fill in the calendar below with the names of the eras. Write the name of the eon if there is no name for the era.

Earth's Historical Calendar

January (31 days)	February (28 days)	March (31 days)	April (30 days)
Hadean eon	Hadean eon	Hadean eon Archean eon	Archean eon
May (31 days)	**June (30 days)**	**July (31 days)**	**August (31 days)**
Archean eon	Archean eon Proterozoic eon	Proterozoic eon	Proterozoic eon
September (30 days)	**October (31 days)**	**November (30 days)**	**December (31 days)**
Proterozoic eon	Proterozoic eon	Proterozoic eon Paleozoic era	Paleozoic era Mesozoic era Cenozoic era

7. How many years in geologic time is represented by one day on the calendar above?

4,600,000,000 ÷ 365 days ≈ 12.6 million years per day

8. On what date does the Proterozoic eon end?

November 19

9. How many days did the Paleozoic era last?

23.2 days

10. How many days are there from the beginning of the Cenozoic era to the end of the year?

5.2 days

Name ______________________ Date ____________ Class ____________

WORKSHEET 46 MATH IN SCIENCE: EARTH SCIENCE

Mapping and Surveying

MATH SKILLS USED
Addition
Multiplication
Division
Decimals
Geometry

Use geometry to analyze maps and solid figures.

When scientists survey an area, they often represent the length, width, and other measurements on a map or diagram. This data can then be used in mathematical equations to determine the area of a piece of land, the volume of a lake, or the dimensions of a mountainside.

Part 1: Perimeter and Area

	Rectangle	Triangle	Odd shapes
	a, b	a, b, c, d	
Perimeter	(2 × a) + (2 × b)	a + b + c	Divide or approximate to a combination of rectangles and triangles, and add their perimeters or areas.
Area	a × b	$\frac{c \times d}{2}$	

The map below shows a survey of a park. Each square of the grid represents one square meter, or 1 m². Use the equations above to answer the questions below.

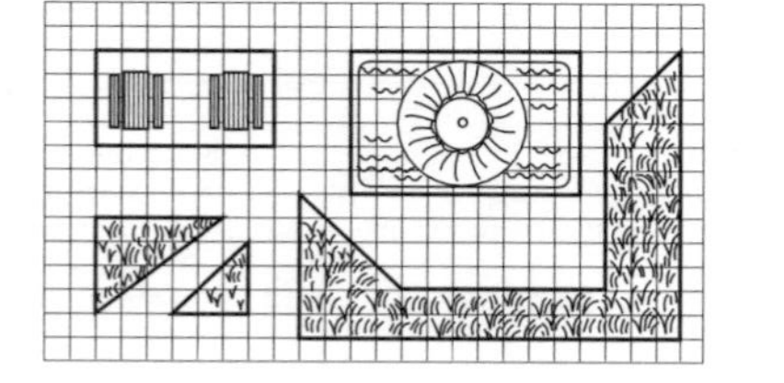

Map It Out!

1. How long is the perimeter of the picnic area?

   7 m + 7 m + 4 m + 4 m = 22 m

2. What is the total area of the picnic area?

   7 m × 4 m = 28 m²

3. How much area in the park has grass?

   10 m² + 4.5 m² + 8 m² + 30 m² + 21 m² + 4.5 m² = 78 m²

4. Estimate the area covered by the fountain, not including the rectangular pool.

   Area of fountain = total area of the pool − visible area of the pool = 54 m² - 32 m² = about 20 m²

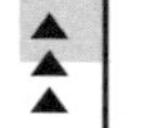

Name ______________________ Date ____________ Class ____________

Part 2: Calculating Volume

To find the volume of a cube or prism, multiply the height times the width times the length, as follows:

Volume = 5 m × 8 m × 15 m
Volume = **600 m³**

Use the equation for volume to answer the following questions:

5. Each fish in the aquarium shown at right needs 3500 cm³ of water to live comfortably. Do the fish in this tank have enough space?

   18 cm × 20 cm × 30 cm = 10,800 cm³; 10,800 cm³ ÷ 3 = 3600 cm³;

   Yes, they have enough space.

6. The Burnside family vegetable garden measures 4 m × 3.5 m. A garden planning guide suggests mixing fertilizer with the soil to a depth of 25 cm. In cubic meters, what will be the total volume of fertilizer-soil mix in the garden?

   25 cm = 0.25 m; 4 m × 3.5 m × 0.25 m = 3.5 m³; The total volume will be 3.5 m³.

A Lock System

A lock is an enclosed part of a canal or waterway equipped with gates that allow the water level in each lock to be changed. Locks are used to raise or lower boats from one level to another.

7. Lock A is 8 m deep, 16 m wide, and 22 m long. What is the capacity of the lock?

   8 m × 16 m × 22 m = 2816 m³

Challenge Yourself!

8. Lock B, which is the same width as Lock A, is 1.5 times as long and has a volume of 4488 m³. How deep is Lock B?

   1.5 × 22 m = 33 m; 33 m × 16 m = 528 m²; 4488 m³ ÷ 528 m² = 8.5 m

Name ______ Date ______ Class ______

WORKSHEET 47 MATH IN SCIENCE: PHYSICAL SCIENCE

Average Speed in a Pinewood Derby

MATH SKILLS USED: Addition, Subtraction, Multiplication, Division, Averages, Decimals, Percentages

Determine the average speeds of a Pinewood Derby car.

Cindy and Santiago have just finished building model cars for their school's annual Pinewood Derby. In order to test their cars, Santiago sets Cindy's car at the top of a 240 cm long ramp and releases it. Cindy uses a stopwatch to measure how long it takes the car to reach the bottom of the ramp. The two decide to conduct three trials for each car and then calculate the overall average speeds. Cindy recorded her initial results in the table below.

Cindy's Car

Trial	Time (s)	Average speed (cm/s)
1	8	30
2	10	24
3	8	30

The Race Is On!

1. Complete the third column of the chart, and show your work below.

   240 cm ÷ 8 s = 30 cm/s; 240 cm ÷ 10 s = 24 cm/s; 240 cm ÷ 8 s = 30 cm/s

2. What was the overall average speed of Cindy's car?

   30 + 24 + 30 = 84; 84 ÷ 3 = 28 cm/s

3. Santiago's car has an overall average speed of 25 cm/s. If he could increase his car's overall average speed by 10%, what would his car's new overall average speed be?

   25 × 0.1 = 2.5; 25 + 2.5 = 27.5; The overall average speed would be 27.5 cm/s.

4. By adding lubricant to the wheels of his car, Santiago determines that he can increase his car's average speed to 29.5 cm/s. What percentage increase does this represent?

   29.5 cm/s − 25 cm/s = 4.5 cm/s; 4.5 ÷ 25 = 0.18 = 18%

Name ______ Date ______ Class ______

WORKSHEET 48 MATH IN SCIENCE: PHYSICAL SCIENCE

Newton: Force and Motion

MATH SKILLS USED: Subtraction, Multiplication, Decimals, Scientific Notation

Use the equations for acceleration and Newton's second law to learn about the motions and forces in the world around us.

In the seventeenth century, a brilliant young scientist named Isaac Newton explained the relationship between force, mass, and acceleration. This simple relationship describes much of the force and motion in the universe, from a tossed baseball to the motion of the stars and planets.

Part 1: Acceleration

Have you ever seen the start of an auto race? In one instant, the cars are practically motionless. The next instant, they are almost flying around the track. What acceleration! But did you know that as a speeding car slows to turn, it is also accelerating? **Acceleration** is defined as the rate at which the velocity of an object changes. In other words, acceleration is a measure of how quickly something speeds up *or* slows down. The equation for acceleration is given below.

EQUATION: change in velocity = final velocity − initial velocity

$$\text{acceleration} = \frac{\text{change in velocity}}{\text{time}}$$

SAMPLE PROBLEM: What is the acceleration of an in-line skater who increases her velocity from 3.5 m/s forward to 6 m/s forward in 2 seconds?

change in velocity = 6 m/s − 3.5 m/s = 2.5 m/s

$$\text{acceleration} = \frac{2.5\ \text{m/s}}{2\ \text{s}}$$

acceleration = **1.25 m/s² forward**

1. Calculate the acceleration of the ball for each time period that it falls.

   a. 9.8 m/s² downward

   b. 9.8 m/s² downward

   c. 9.8 m/s² downward

Challenge Yourself!

2. A jet flying at 200 m/s north accelerates at a rate of 18.2 m/s² for 15 seconds. What is the jet's final velocity?

   18.2 m/s² × 15 seconds = 273 m/s;

   273 m/s + 200 m/s = 473 m/s north

ANSWER KEY

Name ______________________ Date ____________ Class ____________

Part 2: Newton's Second Law

Isaac Newton expressed the relationship between force, mass, and acceleration in his second law. This law is so important that it became the basis for much of modern physics. In fact, Newton's contribution to science was so great that the unit for force, the newton (N), was named after him. A newton is defined as the force needed to produce an acceleration of 1 m/s² on a 1 kg object. Therefore, 1 N = 1 kg × 1 m/s². The equation for Newton's second law is given below.

EQUATION: Force = mass × acceleration

$$F = m \times a$$

If you know two of the values in this equation, you can calculate the third by changing the equation around, as follows:

$$\text{acceleration} = \frac{\text{Force}}{\text{mass}} \quad \textit{and} \quad \text{mass} = \frac{\text{Force}}{\text{acceleration}}$$

SAMPLE PROBLEM: A soccer ball accelerates at a rate of 22 m/s² forward when kicked by a player. The soccer ball has a mass of 0.5 kg. How much force was applied to the ball to produce this acceleration?

Force = mass × acceleration
Force = 0.5 kg × 22 m/s²
Force = 11 kg × m/s²
Force = **11 N**

Use the equations above to complete the following problems:

3. Calculate the force necessary to accelerate the following vehicles at the rate of acceleration shown in the illustration.

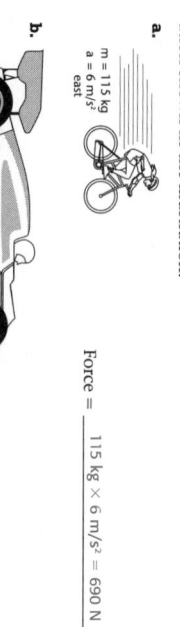

a. m = 115 kg, a = 6 m/s² east

Force = 115 kg × 6 m/s² = 690 N

b.

m = 3950 kg, a = 25 m/s² north

3950 kg × 25 m/s² = 98,750 N

c. m = 14,056 kg, a = 112 m/s² west

14,056 kg × 112 m/s² = 1,574,272 N

Name ______________________ Date ____________ Class ____________

4. How much force is needed to move a 0.1 kg snowball at a rate of 15 m/s² upward?

0.1 kg × 15 m/s² = 1.5 N

5. A 0.02 N push accelerates a table-tennis ball along a table at 8 m/s² north. What is the mass of the ball?

0.02 N ÷ 8 m/s² = 0.0025 kg

6. At lift-off, an astronaut on the space shuttle experiences an acceleration of approximately 35 m/s² upward. What force does an 80 kg astronaut experience during this acceleration?

80 kg × 35 m/s² = 2800 N

7. What is the acceleration of a train with a mass of 3.2×10^9 kg that pushes itself forward with 2.4×10^{10} N of force?

(2.4×10^{10}) N ÷ (3.2×10^9) kg = 0.75 × 10 = 7.5; 7.5 m/s² forward

Part 3: The Force of Gravity

Forces are not always exerted on objects by direct physical contact, such as a hand pushing a door closed. For instance, the Earth exerts the force of gravity on objects even when the objects are not directly touching the ground. The acceleration on an object due to the force of gravity is 9.8 m/s² downward. In other words, for every second an object is falling, its velocity increases by 9.8 m/s downward.

8. a. A 9 kg bowling ball rolls off a table and strikes the ground. If the ball is in the air for 0.5 seconds, how fast is the ball moving when it hits the ground?

0.5 s × 9.8 m/s² = 4.9 m/s downward

b. Another bowling ball with one-fifth less mass rolls off the same table and strikes the ground. When this ball hits the ground, is it moving faster, slower, or the same speed as the first ball? Explain your answer.

The ball with less mass will be traveling the same velocity (4.9 m/s downward) as the first ball.

The difference in mass does not affect the acceleration due to gravity.

Name ______________ Date ________ Class ________

WORKSHEET 49 **MATH IN SCIENCE: PHYSICAL SCIENCE**

MATH SKILLS USED
Multiplication
Decimals

Momentum

Use the equation for momentum to describe an object's motion.

Imagine yourself speeding down a hill on your bicycle without using your brakes. As you reach the bottom of the hill, do you stop? No, you keep on going, until a force, such as the friction between your tires and the road or your brakes, brings you to a stop. The faster you are going or the more mass you have, the more force will be necessary to bring you to a stop. This property is **momentum** (p), which is the product of the mass of an object and its velocity. In an equation, it looks like this:

EQUATION: momentum = mass × velocity

$$p = m \times v$$

SAMPLE PROBLEM: A gymnast with a mass of 62 kg runs at a velocity of 11 m/s toward a pommel horse. What is her momentum?

momentum = mass × velocity

p = 62 kg × 11 m/s

p = **682 kg × m/s toward the pommel horse**

Momentous Momentum

Use the equation for momentum to answer the following questions. Show your work.

1. Find the momentum of the different balls.

m = 0.045 kg, v = 16 m/s upward	m = 0.168 kg, v = 3 m/s forward	m = 0.575 kg, v = 9.2 m/s east
p = 0.045 kg × 16 m/s = 0.72 kg × m/s upward	p = 0.168 kg × 3 m/s = 0.504 kg × m/s forward	p = 0.575 kg × 9.2 m/s = 5.29 kg × m/s east

2. At a rodeo, a bucking bronco throws an 81 kg rider into the air at a velocity of 10 m/s upward. What is the rider's momentum?

   p = 81 kg × 10 m/s = 810 kg × m/s upward

3. Two passengers are riding in a boat that has a mass of 1500 kg. The two passengers together have a mass of 180 kg. What is the momentum of the boat and passengers when the boat is traveling at a velocity of 15 m/s west?

   p = 1500 kg + 180 kg = 1680 kg; 1680 kg × 15 m/s = 25,200 kg × m/s west

Challenge Yourself!

4. What is the velocity of a 55 kg skater who has a momentum of 440 kg × m/s forward?

   440 kg × m/s ÷ 55 kg = 8 m/s forward

Name ______________ Date ________ Class ________

WORKSHEET 50 **MATH IN SCIENCE: PHYSICAL SCIENCE**

MATH SKILLS USED
Addition
Multiplication

Balancing Chemical Equations

Learn to balance chemical equations.

A **chemical equation** is an easy way to represent a chemical reaction—it shows you which elements react together and what the resulting products will be. In the equation, the reactants are on the left side of the arrow, and the products are on the right side of the arrow. A balanced chemical equation has an equal number of atoms of each element in the reactants and the products.

PROCEDURE: To balance a chemical reaction, count the number of atoms of each element in both the reactants and the products. Then determine the numbers that, when multiplied by the number of atoms in the reactants or products, will make the number of atoms on either side of the arrow equal. These numbers are known as *coefficients*. Next check the equation by counting the number of atoms in the reactants and the products. If the equation is balanced, the number of atoms on each side will be the same.

SAMPLE PROBLEM: $Zn + HBr \rightarrow H_2 + ZnBr_2$

Step 1: Count the number of atoms of each element in the reactants and in the products.

Step 2: Determine the number that, when multiplied by the one or more atoms in the reactants or products, will make the number of atoms on either side of the arrow equal. Because we have two H atoms and two Br atoms in the product, we can multiply the reactant HBr by a coefficient of 2, as follows:

$$Zn + \mathbf{2}HBr \rightarrow H_2 + ZnBr_2$$

Step 3: Check the equation by counting the number of atoms of each element on each side of the equation. Because there are the same number of atoms of each element in the reactants and the products, you know the equation is balanced.

Step 1

Reactants	Products
1 Zn	1 Zn
1 H	2 H
1 Br	2 Br

Step 3

Reactants	Products
1 Zn	1 Zn
2 H	2 H
2 Br	2 Br

A Balancing Act

Balance the following chemical equations:

1. $Na + Cl_2 \rightarrow NaCl$ — $2Na + Cl_2 \rightarrow 2NaCl$
2. $Ca + Cl_2 \rightarrow CaCl_2$ — Balanced
3. $H_2O \rightarrow H_2 + O_2$ — $2H_2O \rightarrow 2H_2 + O_2$
4. $Cu + AgCl \rightarrow Ag + CuCl_2$ — $Cu + 2AgCl \rightarrow 2Ag + CuCl_2$
5. $FeCl_2 + K_2S \rightarrow FeS + KCl$ — $FeCl_2 + K_2S \rightarrow FeS + 2KCl$

ANSWER KEY

Name ______ Date ______ Class ______

WORKSHEET 51 MATH IN SCIENCE: PHYSICAL SCIENCE

Work and Power

MATH SKILLS USED
Addition
Multiplication
Division
Decimals
Scientific Notation

Use the equations for work and power.

Part 1: An Equation for Work

As you sit and read this worksheet, are you doing work? You might say, "Yes, of course." But are you doing work in the scientific sense? Scientists use the word *work* to describe a very specific concept. In physics, **work** is a force applied over a distance.

EQUATION: work = Force × distance

$$W = F \times d$$

The SI unit for work is the newton-meter (N · m), also known as a **joule (J).** You can calculate the amount of work accomplished with the equation above. Let's see how it's done!

SAMPLE PROBLEM: How much work is done on a 16 N sack of potatoes when you lift the sack 1.5 m?

$$W = 16 \text{ N} \times 1.5 \text{ m}$$
$$W = \mathbf{24\ J}$$

Work It Out!

Based on what you know about work, answer the following questions. Be sure to show your work.

1. A deflated hot-air balloon weighs a total of 8000 N. Filled with hot air, the balloon rises to a height of 1000 m. How much work is accomplished by the hot air?

   8000 N × 1000 m = 8,000,000 J

2. A rope is thrown over a beam, and one end is tied to a 300 N bundle of lumber. You pull the free end of the rope 2 m with a force of 400 N to lift the lumber off the ground. How much work have you done?

   400 N × 2 m = 800 J

3. A 150 N boy rides a 60 N bicycle a total of 200 m at a constant speed. The frictional force against the forward motion of the bicycle equals 35 N. How much work does the boy do? Explain your answer. (Hint: Remember that work is only done when the motion is in the same direction that the force is applied.)

   35 N × 200 m = 7000 J; The weights of the boy and the bicycle are not used to calculate the work done because the direction of their forces (downward) is different than the direction of the motion (forward).

Name ______ Date ______ Class ______

Part 2: Work and Power

Work is closely related to the concept of power. **Power** is a measure of how much work is done in a certain time. The faster work is done, the more power is produced.

EQUATION:

$$\text{power} = \frac{\text{work}}{\text{time}}$$

$$P = \frac{W}{t}$$

The unit for power is the **watt (W).** One watt (W) is equal to 1 J of work done for 1 second. Use the data given in the diagram below to determine how much work and power are involved in each step. Remember to show your work.

Force necessary to lift painting = 60 N

Height of ladder = 2 m

Height of stairs = 3 m

Step 1: A 50 N girl climbs the flight of stairs in 3 seconds.

Work = 50 N × 3 m = 150 J

Power = 150 J ÷ 3 s = 50 W

Step 2: The girl lifts a painting to a height of 0.5 m in 0.75 seconds.

Work = 60 N × 0.5 m = 30 J

Power = 30 J ÷ 0.75 seconds = 40 W

Step 3: The girl climbs the ladder with the painting in 5 seconds.

Work = 50 N + 60 N = 110 N
110 N × 2 m = 220 J

Power = 220 J ÷ 5 seconds = 44 W

Challenge Yourself!

4. A crane lifts a load of steel that weighs 9.3×10^5 N a distance of 100 m. It takes 5 minutes to complete the task.
   a. How much work is done by the crane?

      $(9.3 \times 10^5 \text{ N}) \times 100 \text{ m} = 9.3 \times 10^7$ J, or 93,000,000 J

   b. How much power does the crane produce?

      $(9.3 \times 10^7 \text{ J}) \div 300 \text{ seconds} = 3.1 \times 10^5$ W, or 310,000 W

Name ______________ Date ________ Class ________

WORKSHEET 52 MATH IN SCIENCE: PHYSICAL SCIENCE

MATH SKILLS USED
Multiplication
Division
Decimals
Geometry

A Bicycle Trip

Use your math skills to see how the gears of a bicycle transfer energy.

The gears on a bicycle make up a system for transferring energy from the rider's legs to the front sprockets (or gears) and then through the chain to the rear wheel. The 12-speed bicycle below has two front sprockets (*A*) connected to the pedals. The sprockets contain 42 and 52 teeth, respectively. The rear wheel has a diameter of 70 cm. It has six different-sized sprockets (*B*) attached at the center containing 14, 17, 20, 23, 26, and 28 teeth, going from the smallest to the largest sprocket. Front and rear *derailleurs* transfer the chain from one sprocket to another during the process of changing gears. The length of the pedal arm is 15 cm.

Sample Situation

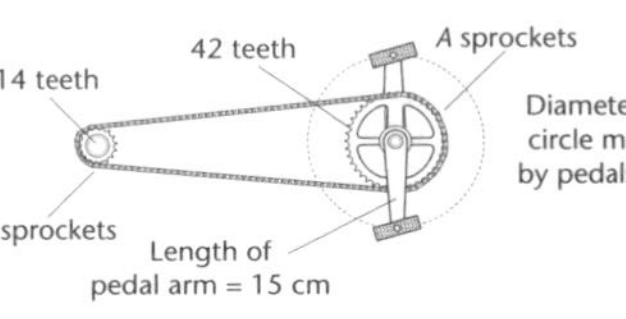

Use What You Know!

Suppose the chain is connected to the smaller sprocket in front, which contains 42 teeth, and to the smallest sprocket in the rear, which contains 14 teeth. Use the sample situation to answer the following questions:

1. When the pedals make one complete rotation, how many teeth in the front sprocket does the chain move over?

42 teeth

2. How many times will the rear sprocket and rear wheel turn during one rotation of the pedals?

42 ÷ 14 = 3; They will turn 3 times.

3. a. What distance will each foot move during one complete turn (rotation) of the pedals? (*Hint:* circumference = 3.14 × diameter)

3.14 × (2 × 15 cm) = 94.2 cm

b. What distance will the rear wheel and bicycle move forward while the pedals make one complete turn?

3 turns × 70 cm × 3.14 = 659.4 cm

4. How many times farther will the rear wheel of the bicycle move compared with the distance the rider's feet moved?

659.4 cm ÷ 94.2 cm = 7; 7 times farther.

MATH IN SCIENCE: PHYSICAL SCIENCE

Name ______________ Date ________ Class ________

5. Using the sample situation from the previous page, fill out the following table:

	Teeth in A	Teeth in B	Wheel turns per pedal turn	Distance (cm) bicycle wheel moves per pedal turn	Distance (cm) pedals move per turn	Ratio of wheel distance to pedal distance
Smallest *A* connected to largest *B*	42	28	42 ÷ 28 = 1.5	1.5 × (3.14 × 70) = 329.7	30 × 3.14 = 94.2	329.7 ÷ 94.2 = 3.5
Smallest *A* connected to second largest *B*	42	26	42 ÷ 26 = 1.6	1.6 × (3.14 × 70) = 351.7	30 × 3.14 = 94.2	351.7 ÷ 94.2 = 3.7
Smallest *A* connected to third largest *B*	42	23	42 ÷ 23 = 1.8	1.8 × (3.14 × 70) = 395.6	30 × 3.14 = 94.2	395.6 ÷ 94.2 = 4.2
Smallest *A* connected to fourth largest *B*	42	20	42 ÷ 20 = 2.1	2.1 × (3.14 × 70) = 461.6	30 × 3.14 = 94.2	461.6 ÷ 94.2 = 4.9
Smallest *A* connected to fifth largest *B*	42	17	42 ÷ 17 = 2.5	2.5 × (3.14 × 70) = 549.5	30 × 3.14 = 94.2	549.5 ÷ 94.2 = 5.8
Smallest *A* connected to smallest *B* (sample from previous page)	42	14	42 ÷ 14 = 3	3 × (3.14 × 70) = 659.4	30 × 3.14 = 94.2	659.4 ÷ 94.2 = 7
Largest *A* connected to largest *B*	52	28	52 ÷ 28 = 1.8	1.8 × (3.14 × 70) = 417.6	30 × 3.14 = 94.2	417.6 ÷ 94.2 = 4.4
Largest *A* connected to second largest *B*	52	26	52 ÷ 26 = 2	2 × (3.14 × 70) = 439.6	30 × 3.14 = 94.2	439.6 ÷ 94.2 = 4.7
Largest *A* connected to third largest *B*	52	23	52 ÷ 23 = 2.3	2.3 × (3.14 × 70) = 505.5	30 × 3.14 = 94.2	505.5 ÷ 94.2 = 5.4
Largest *A* connected to fourth largest *B*	52	20	52 ÷ 20 = 2.6	2.6 × (3.14 × 70) = 571.5	30 × 3.14 = 94.2	571.5 ÷ 94.2 = 6.1
Largest *A* connected to fifth largest *B*	52	17	52 ÷ 17 = 3.1	3.1 × (3.14 × 70) = 681.4	30 × 3.14 = 94.2	681.4 ÷ 94.2 = 7.2
Largest *A* connected to smallest *B*	52	14	52 ÷ 14 = 3.7	3.7 × (3.14 × 70) = 813.3	30 × 3.14 = 94.2	813.3 ÷ 94.2 = 8.6

Challenge Yourself!

6. Which *A* sprocket connected to which *B* sprocket will achieve the greatest distance?

The largest *A* sprocket connected to the smallest *B* sprocket

7. What arrangement of the gears will give the least multiplication of the distance?

The smallest *A* sprocket connected to the largest *B* sprocket

ANSWER KEY

Name ______________________ Date ____________ Class ____________

WORKSHEET 53 MATH IN SCIENCE: PHYSICAL SCIENCE

MATH SKILLS USED: Division, Decimals

Mechanical Advantage

Use the equation for mechanical advantage to see how machines multiply force.

The **mechanical advantage** of a machine is the factor by which the machine multiplies force. The mechanical advantage of a machine can be used to determine how well a machine works and whether it can perform a particular job.

EQUATION: $\text{mechanical advantage } (MA) = \dfrac{\text{output force}}{\text{input force}}$

SAMPLE PROBLEM: What is the mechanical advantage of a lever that requires an input force of 20 N and lifts an object that weighs 60 N?

$$\text{mechanical advantage } (MA) = \frac{60 \text{ N}}{20 \text{ N}}$$

$$MA = \mathbf{3}$$

Practice Your Skills!

Use the equation for mechanical advantage to answer the following questions:

1. Amanda uses a wheelbarrow to lift a load of bricks. The bricks weigh 600 N, which is more than Amanda could normally carry. However, with the wheelbarrow, Amanda can lift the bricks with as little as 120 N. What is the mechanical advantage of the wheelbarrow?

   MA = 600 N ÷ 120 N = 5

2. Marshall wants to remove a tree stump from the ground. To do this, he puts one end of a long beam under the stump and puts all of his weight on the other end. His weight is just enough to lift the stump. The stump weighs 400 N. Marshall weighs 250 N. What is the mechanical advantage of the lever Marshall is using?

   MA = 400 N ÷ 250 N = 1.6

3. A system of pulleys allows a mechanic to lift an 1800 N engine.

   a. If the mechanic exerts a force of 600 N on the pulley system, what is the mechanical advantage of the machine?

   MA = 1800 N ÷ 600 N = 3

   b. What is the mechanical advantage of the pulley system if the mechanic must exert 800 N of force to lift the engine?

   MA = 1800 N ÷ 800 N = 2.25

   c. After improving the design of his pulley system, the mechanic can now lift the engine with a MA of 4. How much force is now required to lift the engine?

   1800 N ÷ 4 N = 450 N

Name ______________________ Date ____________ Class ____________

WORKSHEET 54 MATH IN SCIENCE: PHYSICAL SCIENCE

MATH SKILLS USED: Multiplication, Scientific Notation, SI Measurement and Conversion

Color at Light Speed

Analyze the wavelength and frequency of the colors in light.

Visible light consists of a range of different colors that combine to form white light. This range is called the **color spectrum.** Each color in the color spectrum has a unique wavelength and frequency. Our eyes see light of different wavelengths as different colors. The frequency (f) and wavelength (λ) of visible light can be used to determine the speed of light (υ) by the following equation:

$$\text{speed of light} = \text{frequency} \times \text{wavelength}$$

$$\upsilon = f \times \lambda$$

The frequency of waves is measured in waves per second, or hertz (Hz). The wavelength can be measured as the distance between two wave crests. The diagram below shows the spectrum of visible light with the corresponding wavelengths for each color. As you can see, the wavelengths of visible light fall in the range of 400 nanometers (nm) to 750 nm. One nanometer is equal to 0.000000001 m.

UV ← Violet | Blue | Green | Yellow | Orange | Red → IR

400 nm — 500 nm — 600 nm — 700 nm

1. Calculate the speed of light for the following. Show your work.

   a. a shade of yellow light with a wavelength of 5.8×10^{-7} m and a frequency of 5.17×10^{14} Hz

   (5.8×10^{-7}) m/wave × (5.17×10^{14}) waves/s = 3.0×10^{8} m/s

   b. a shade of red light with a wavelength of 6.98×10^{-7} m and a frequency of 4.3×10^{14} Hz

   (6.98×10^{-7}) m/wave × (4.3×10^{14}) waves/s = 3.0×10^{8} m/s

   c. a shade of violet light with a wavelength of 4×10^{-6} m and a frequency of 7.5×10^{13} Hz

   (4×10^{-6}) m/wave × (7.5×10^{13}) waves/s = 3.0×10^{8} m/s

   d. What can you conclude about the speed of light of different colors?

   The speed of light is the same no matter what the wavelength or frequency is.

Name ______________________ Date ____________ Class ____________

Color at Light Speed, continued

2. a. If the speed of light is constant (meaning it does not change), does the wavelength increase or decrease with an increase in frequency?

It decreases.

b. What happens to the wavelength as the frequency decreases?

It increases.

3. Convert the following metric measurements:

a. An orange light with a wavelength of 620 nm is 0.00000062 m long.

b. A blue light with a wavelength of 445 nm is 0.000445 mm long.

c. A violet light with a wavelength of 410 nm is 0.00041 cm long.

d. A green light with a wavelength of 550 nm is 0.00000055 m long.

4. The relationship between the energy of a light wave and its frequency is given in the following equation:

$$E = h \times f$$

In this equation, f is the frequency and h is a constant.

a. Which of the colors from question 1 has the most energy?

Violet

b. Which color has the least energy?

Red

c. What is the relationship between the frequency of a light wave and its energy?

The higher the frequency is, the greater the energy is.

d. What is the relationship between the wavelength of a light wave and its energy?

The shorter the wavelength is, the greater the energy is.